Bulbophyllums:

The Incomplete Guide;

From A to Why?

2-2013

Esther -

Good Growing

Bill Thomas

Bulbophyllums:

The Incomplete Guide;

From A to Why?

Bill Thoms

Front cover: Bulb. A-doribil Candy Ann 'Lavender Lady'

Inside front flap,
top: *Bulb. sigaldiae* 'Fuzzy Wine'
bottom: Bulb. Frank Smith 'The King' CCE/AOS 96pts

Back cover, top row;
Left,   *Bulb. annandalei* 'A-doribil' FCC/AOS (photo by Jim Clarkson)
Right,   *Bulb. flabellum-veneris* from the Philippines

Middle row;
Left,   Bulb. Frank Smith 'Golden Star'
Right,   Bulb. Jim Clarkson 'Bill Thoms' FCC/AOS (photo by Jim Clarkson)

Bottom row;
Left,   Bulb. Vicky Leighty 'A-doribil' HCC/AOS (photo by Ernest Walters)
Next top, *Bulb. macrobulbum* 'Magnifico' CHM-AM/AOS
bottom, *Bulb. lindleyanum*
Next,   Bulb. A-doribil Collin 'Peppermint' HCC/AOS
Far right, *Bulb. frostii* 'A-doribil'

Thanks to my late mother, Cindy Banks, for instilling in me a lifelong sense of curiosity and offbeat humor.

Thanks to my wife, friend and best grower in the world, Doris Dukes, for all her proofreading, advice and support lo these many, long years.

Thanks to Barry Woolf of Maryland for all his help and expertise with scanning, cleaning up the photos and bringing me into the 21st century with presentations. He was instrumental in getting me to dig my book out of mothballs and get to work on it again. He also has made it possible to put it into a CD. (Woolfphoto1@comcast.net)

Thanks to Leonard Ingalls of Texas, for his generous help in encouraging and steering me in the proper direction to produce this book, as well as up-sizing my low resolution pictures (over & over & over) and answering my myriad technical questions. (Leonardingalls.com).

Thanks to Jim and Emily Clarkson; he - for the wonderful lab work with my open seed pods and his great photographs, she - for the classy lady she is.

Thanks to Ken Roberts for his invaluable help tracking down information in obscure books, magazines and journals for my research. He has always been quick to suggest where to go and how to get there (the good kind of destination).

Thanks to Don and Polly Wilson, and their daughter, Karen, photographers extraordinaire, for their wonderful photographs and the care they always took with my plants, unlike the "Crisper".

EXTRA SPECIAL thanks to Frank Smith, (the finest hybridizer in the world), of Krull-Smith Nursery, for sharing his expertise in breeding, for helping me to realize the subtle, yet important qualities in flowers, for donating his lab and giving me time and space to grow my crosses. Without his extreme generosity and friendship, I would never have been able to approach my goal of producing top quality new hybrids.

Finally, I want to dedicate this book to the memory of my dad, William Davis Thoms, Sr., who taught me that learning can be fun.

Thanks to the many photographers who allowed me to use their work in this book;

Greg Allikas,
Allen Black,
Edwin S. Boyett,
E. "Chaps" Chapman,
James Clarkson,
Lewis Ellsworth,
James Harris,
Brian Kelly,
Monroe Kokin,
Tom McGuigan,
Jay Norris,
Phongsawat Phinhiran,
Yanyong Punpreuk,
Mark Alan Reinke,
Charles Rowden,
M.E. "Pete" Thompson;
Ernest Walters,
Bill Williams,
Johanna Tjeenk Willink and
Don, Polly and Karen Wilson.

Without their contributions and award photographs, the flowers would simply be a distant memory.

<u>DISCLAIMER!!!</u>

The ideas and suggestions in this book are intended to be helpful. They refer mostly to growing bulbophyllums.
Many Caribbean genera (Broughtonias, Tolumnias, Encyclias and Psychilus, to name a few) are adapted to drying out faster since that is the prevailing weather pattern in their part of the world. Many Central African genera go through long, long dry spells for the same reason.

<u>If you are having no problems and everything is growing just fine, don't change.</u>

The growing ideas presented here work fine for me in Central Florida, USA, but, there are exceptions to everything, so if you try something and it doesn't work out, you must be the exception. Don't be angry, think of yourself as **SPECIAL**.

<u>This book is a work of WHIMSY. Any relation to a serious project either current or past is purely coincidental.</u>

Also….

Enjoy this book or Misty sleeps with the fishes!

Table of Contents

Unless otherwise listed, all photographs are by the author.

Ready To Dive Into Bulbophyllums?

©Doris Dukes

On a waterfall in Brazil, 1996

<u>Chapter 1</u>
<u>Introduction</u>

Why? Because, it's not fair - not to share.
And if not now, when?

Welcome to the wonderful, weird and wacky world of the
BULBOPHYLLUMS.
Do not be afraid. Some say it's the largest genus in all the orchid family. Who knows? Who cares? I only know there are a zillion of 'em (actually, more than 2800 species) and they have the weirdest names you ever tried to pronounce. Anyway, let's get started on our journey, we have a lot to cover and only a lifetime.
***Bulbophyllum* Thou.**
    First of all, the genus is pronounced bulb-oh-**fill'**-um because of the two 'lls' and not **'fye-lum'**. The letters after the genus, Thou., stand for Louie-Marie Aubert du Petit-Thouars, who first described it. I know, where do they get these names? It turns out after careful and exhaustive investigation that he received his name from his parents, Louie and Marie who were found missing after a giant surprise birthday purge (I made that up). But, just for fun, and to be scientifically proper and as accurate as possible, there will be names (or their abbreviations) listed after the species (pronounced, spee' - shees). Those letters designate the authors who described them. That way, you can tell it's the plant described by Schlecter and not Kraenzlin. I know, who cares, they're only going to change them, but I hope this will be read by lots of people and some of them are sooooo picky.
    Secondly, I'm going to presume, (not assume), that some of the readers of this book are not long-time scientifically trained botanists, and start from scratch. I know that doesn't apply to you. I know that when you look right and left all you see are mere mortals. I also know that about now you want to go into your wallet and send me pieces of paper with pictures of dead presidents. I will accept them gratefully and graciously.
    Anyway, this book is supposed to be helpful to the beginner, (which means easy to understand) as well as to those more advanced, (which means more informative). Ha Ha. We'll just see about that.
    Plant names are broken down into two parts, the first is the genus (jee'-nus), [plural, genera, (jen'-er-ah)] which puts the plant into a broad category like Cattleya, Disa, Paphiopedilum, or in this case Bulbophyllum. The second name is the species name (or hybrid name). Finally, the species name is followed by the name or names of the authors who first described it. If a plant is reclassified by another student (all taxonomists are called students), the first author's name is

put in parentheses followed by the author of the change. That way, if you want to show off, after doing some research, you can point out that *Bulbophyllum guttulatum* (Hook.f.) N.P. Balakr. means that a plant originally identified as *Cirrhopetalum guttulatum* by the son of Sir William Jackson Hooker (Hooker, filia; whose name was Sir Joseph Dalton Hooker) was reclassified as *Bulbophyllum guttulatum* by Nambiyath Puthansurayil Balakrishnan. Here is a positive note (for some). All the plants have been re-combined back into *Bulbophyllum* which means there is only one name to remember, so forget *Megaclinium, Trias, Mastigion, Cirrhopetalum* or any of the others.

Isn't this fun?

The full name of a species is written:

Bulbophyllum lobbii Lindl.

It can be shortened to *Bulb. lobbii* Lindl. or

when discussing many different plants of the

same genus (in the same publication), *B. lobbii* Lindl.

To designate different forms (or varieties) of the same species (for instance, white or spotted, if it has been properly written up in an accepted journal), all plants exhibiting that characteristic are referred to as *variety albina* (al – **bean'**-ah) or *variety maculata* (mack – you – **lot'** – ah) respectively, and written (for example) as *Bulb. sulawesii var. maculata* Garay, et al. (et al. stands for et alia, meaning "and others", which in this case are Hamer & Siegerist).

Alba means white and may not be used if the flower has any other color in it. Flowers lacking any pigmentation in the anthocyanin (**an'** – tho – **sigh'** – an – in) group (reds and blues) may be referred to as albino but not alba. For instance, flowers might be yellow (and called flavum) instead of the normal color.

Since plants are rarely shown with their authors, it looks awkward when discussing them in print. I will use the author the first time for each species, but leave it out afterward.

To designate one plant from another in the same grex, (pronounced, grecks, and meaning a group of plants with the same hybrid name), a special name can be given to each plant. These are clonal names and start with capital letters, are set off with one quote mark and are not italicized as in, *Bulb. lobbii* 'Kathy's Gold' (owned by Kathy Klett of Tropical Orchid Farm in Maui). If the plant wins an award, the award is listed as well. So you have,

Bulb. lobbii 'Kathy's Gold' AM/AOS

which is an Award of Merit from the American Orchid Society.

The full name of a hybrid is written with capital letters at the beginning of each word like this:

Bulb. Stars And Stripes   or

Bulb. Elizabeth Ann 'Buckleberry' FCC\AOS

I like to put the name of the parents on the back of a plants' tag since it is impossible to remember all the names. In the case of Bulb. Elizabeth Ann, it would be written as: =(*longissimum X rothschildianum*). The plant that held the seedpod is strangely enough called the pod parent and is listed first. Guess what the plant that donated the pollen is called? Righto! The pollen parent. Sometimes, it almost seems there could be hope for scientific describers, but then …

We have a big problem with the Bulbophyllum genus and its many off-shoots, sub-genera and sections that have been split away or joined together over the years. Beyond the less critical problem of what is allied to what, the greater problem with hybrid names must be addressed before going further.

The world's accepted orchid-naming authority is the International Orchid Registrar, which is part of the Royal Horticultural Society of England. The three criteria to be classified a Bulbophyllum are:

1. The plant must have only one joint in the bulb (a dendrobium can have more than 25);

2. The inflorescence must arise from the base of the plant

or along the rhizome...and

3. The lip must be mobile;

They (in this case the culprits are taxonomists and their enablers) have determined that all the plants with these characteristics are bulbophyllums, regardless of similarities or differences. If it were a perfect world, you and I would already be in charge. Some say it's good we're not. Shows how much they know.

Back to the fun.

Hybrids are never italicized and always start with a CAPITAL LETTER. The exception (never say never) is a natural hybrid produced in the wild, which still is italicized and starts with a small letter x followed by the name, such as:

Cattleya xclaesiana   =(*intermedia X loddigesii*)

The same hybrid artificially made is treated just like a normal hybrid, C. Claesiana. That way you can tell its history.

If you haven't learned anything yet nor been amused by these ramblings, you are both a very learned individual and possessed with an overabundance of recalcitrance to the therapeutic aspects of jocularity. Take heart! I left in several mistakes on purpose. I know some people look for errors and I want to please everyone so your time won't be wasted.

An editor once said to me that to be published by a "Reputable Publishing House", a book on orchids must be entirely scientific, which means no joking around, no asides, no humor of any kind and certainly no deliberate errors. After I finished spitting up my coffee on the front of his shirt, (accidentally, of course), I decided the best course of action was to publish it myself. Therefore, I get to oversee the format and content (such as it is).

I write the way I do because I like to enjoy what I read, and adding humorous things keeps the information from being too dry and makes it easier to remember.... what was I talking about? Oh yeah,

If this book makes you gag, want to throw it in the trash, or worse, I'm sorry...

(for you),

and encourage you to go read one of the other 90,000,000 books that fit the format you enjoy. If you like it, tell Dorie, because she is still rolling her eyes over the style.

FLOWERING STYLES

Speaking of style, let's talk about flowering styles. There are a number of bulbophyllums that come from various African countries and Madagascar that fall into a category called Megaclinium, where the inflorescence is squeezed into flat, rectangular, square, triangular, or all sorts of strange diamond shapes. That inflorescence, or rachis (pronounced ray' kiss) puts them in the Megaclinium Section. They also get a tremendous amount of water for a certain period of time during the year and then they dry off. There is not a lot of culture information about the various bulbophyllums from Africa, other than descriptions from where they come and perhaps some elevations. But it doesn't tell you if it's on the wet side of the mountain or the dry side or whether they grow in many places in Africa where the Bulbophyllums and Sarcanthiniae (sar – can – thin' – ee – aye) grow (those are monopodial orchids which continue growing up from the base (for example Angraecum), unlike sympodial orchids which grow sideways from the base like Cattleyas).

In many of these areas, it's so unbelievably dry you can't imagine in your wildest dreams that orchids actually grow there, or epiphytes of any kind. But they do. And so, I found that with the bulbophyllum group Megaclinium, they still respond to water for longer periods. It just has to be the right period.

They have very thin roots that will work their way down to the water and they will wick up the water quite a bit. And as long as the roots have water to them, the bulbs will stay big, and fat, and swollen. If they are grown in such a manner that they dry off rapidly, the plants will grow but they will always maintain a shriveled look.

Sometimes, it's necessary to go back and forth between having the plants wet for a day or so and then dry out. By wet a day or so, I mean thoroughly wet, where they are sitting in a shallow tray of water (with an edge no more than ¼" high) and have all the water available to them as though it was raining for a day or two at a time. Then following that with a day or so of dry conditions and then more rain makes them really grow. That approximates a lot of the conditions where they live. At certain times during the year it is necessary to dry them out for LONG periods of time and I am not very good at that (not very good? I am incapable of doing that so I don't grow them at all). I know that the B. falcatum (Lindl.) Rchb.f. group seems to grow well and flower easily in the spring but many of the other groups that have an upright rachis, like B. purpureorachis (De Wild.) Schltr., B. scaberulum (Rolfe) Bolus, B. bufo (correctly: B. falcatum v. bufo) (Lindl.) Govaerts, and things like that, seem to be more difficult for me to bloom. Aside from mild blooming in the springtime, that seems to be about it, although on older plants it seems as though the flowering season (for others) can last for a number of months, because the flowers are opening in succession along the rachis and that's one of the things that will differentiate plants among the different sub-sections of the Megaclinium group. Do the flowers open up in succession? One at a time? A few at a time? Or do they open up all along the rachis and are primarily all open at one time?

There is a large group (thanks to Ken Roberts, I know there are 69 species so far) which come from Brazil and surrounding areas that have flowers that open in a variety of ways. There is one called *B. rupicola* Barb. Rodr., which has a little tiny, miniature bulb, and an almost terete leaf. It is a little wedge shaped leaf, grows in very sunny, hot, dry conditions and produces an upright flower spike with very small white flowers that are secund (opening all in one direction). They also seem to grow where the poisonous snake in the viper family, the Fer-de-lance (*Bothrops atrox*) lives. Enjoy.

Several of the other kinds open one or two flowers at a time for a long period of time, *B. weddelii* (Lindl.) Rchb.f., and *B. ipanemense* Hoehne, are two.

Most of the large flowered varieties are from Thailand, down through the Philippines, Indonesia, Borneo, New Guinea, and areas like that. The *B. lobbii* 'Kathy's Gold' clone from Java (also considered *variety colossus*) is about six inches, or fifteen centimeters, top to bottom, and four inches, or ten centimeters, side to side. It has an extremely long pedicel (**ped'** - ih – sill), (the stem that holds the flower to the stalk) and it appears to look like a flower that has moved far away from the plant. However, the inflorescence is only about two centimeters long at maximum and it is actually quite short down along the rhizome. The flowers come from about two bulbs back from the front growth. They don't come from the front growth.

Some plants can either flower on the single front growth, like *B. longissimum* (Ridl.) J.J.Sm., the front and previous years' growths, like *B. echinolabium* J.J.Sm., along the rhizome, like *B. lobbii*, or a weird combination, like *B. fascinator* (Rolfe) Rolfe or *B. lasiochilum* Par. & Rchb.f., which, by the fall, can produce up to three bulbs. At this point, each bulb can give you at least one flower, possibly two. In fact, as long as most of the bulbo plants are warm enough and given sufficient food to meet their needs, they will continue to grow and produce new growths until their flowering time. In this way you can get an awful lot of additional plant in a year and an equal number of extra flowers. When the plants are bursting with vigor, many unusual things can occur.

One *B. longissimum* plant that we have has produced three spikes out of one bulb but that plant is an exception. Mostly they produce one inflorescence per bulb. However, *B. lepidum* [correctly: *flabellum-veneris* (J. Konig) Aver.], and the other plants in the Cirrhopetalum Section will produce, easily, three, and sometimes up to five inflorescences per bulb. If you get multiple front bulbs, and multiple growths per year, during the flowering cycle you'll find that you can get, instead of one front with one flower spike, you have a half a dozen flowering bulbs with three to five spikes, which very quickly becomes almost thirty inflorescences. They're not produced all at one time, but they are produced over a period of several months so the plants are in bloom for quite a long period of time with no bad smell.

Plants in the Sestochilus Section (*B. lobbii, B. facetum* Garay et al., etc.), Hyalosema Section (*B. grandiflorum* Blume, *B. burfordiense* Garay, Hamer and Siegerist, etc.), Ephippium Section like *B. blumei* (Lindl.) J.J.Sm., and Leptopus Section; *B. elassoglossum* Siegerist, and others, will flower all along the stem. So, the longer and more stems that you can get, the more possible flowering places you have.

There are some plants in the Intervallatae Section, like *B. macrochilum* Rolfe, and the Dialepanthe Section, like *B. digoelense* J.J.Sm. that produce an inflorescence that has flowers one after another, after another, for up to a year and a half, maybe longer. Plants in the Lepidorhiza Section like *B. carunculatum* Garay, et al, *B. echinolabium, B. levanae* Ames, *B. sulawesii* Garay, et al, *B. mandibulare* Rchb.f., *B. cootesii* M.A. Clem. and *B. orthoglossum* Kraenzl., produce inflorescences out of the front bulb at first, back bulbs later and continue for several years after that to produce flowers one after another, after another. Usually, they wind up with about eight or ten flowers but can go to 18 or 20.

B. rothschildianum (O'Brien) J.J.Sm., *B. longissimum* (Ridl.) J.J.Sm., *B. fascinator* (Rolfe) Rolfe and most hybrids with them primarily flower in the fall. By then they have produced whatever growths they are going to produce. In the fall during the cooling and drying out period, they produce their flowers. They primarily flower during that one time, (that's September to January here in central Florida). Some *B. fascinators* will flower as early as July but the majority seems to be October or November.

Another feature is the way they flower. Some plants like *B. elassoglossum* Siegerist and *B. pardalotum* Garay et al., open their flowers in the early morning and close up by about ten AM. Plants in the Sestochilus Section close their flowers at night for the first few days and seem to accept pollen better if you wait until they stay open all the time. You can use the pollen right away, but the stigmatic surface (where the pollen goes) seems to be more receptive later. If a flower has an odor (and some bulbos, especially in the Lepidorhiza Section, have a lot – sheesh) it is best to make the cross when the odor is the strongest, since the odor is there to attract the pollinator.

So, as you can see, flowers come from the front bulbs, from previous years' bulbs and from all along the rhizomes in a variety of manners and the flowers open in lots of different ways.

Chapter 2
Habitat

This area of the world, from Tropical Africa and Madagascar in the west, to India, Malaysia and Indo-China in the north and through Indonesia south to New Guinea and North Australia encompasses the main regions of Bulbophyllum habitats for warm growing species in the genus. There are more areas around the world, but this is the main center.

This is the Indo-Pacific basin from where most of the great plants originate. It covers millions of square miles and most of those are mountainous. The main similarity is moisture in the air. Lots of it for long periods of time.

This is what it looks like in the forest. This is Borneo, but it could be almost any-where. The thin tree on the right is loaded with orchids because seeds germinate and grow where the light is lower. Mostly, they won't flower, though, until the tree on the left falls down from age, wind, lightning or storm. Then they will get enough light to bloom.

Rain and fog don't show up well in pictures, which is why they have fake rain in the movies. In order for the fog to show up this much in the photo, it was so foggy I couldn't see ten feet in front of me. I took the shot and only saw the far trees when I developed the slide. The air is VERY moist. Plants can get a lot of water this way even if it doesn't rain.

No discussion of habitat would be complete without pointing out that one of the main reasons plants grow on the trees and not in the ground is due in part to the fact that there isn't much "food value" in the soil. Actually, there isn't much soil at all above the underlying sand or rocks. This is true in all rain or cloud forests around the world. There is a lot of food in the air and in the rain, so plants take advantage of this (along with higher light and air movement) by growing in trees and absorbing the food before it gets to the ground.

Cleaned, brightened, focused and sharpened by Barry Woolf

Original

If you're in the woods and run across an Orang-utan, (literally: man of the forest; even if this is a female), don't forget to keep the 4 foot long arms in mind. While I was trying to make sure the focus was right and the face was centered while squinting through the eyepiece, she reached out and grabbed my ear. As I launched myself backwards into the Japanese family hiding behind me, I set foreign relations back quite a bit.

Where they grow

Bulbophyllums are the most widespread genus of orchid in the world, occurring throughout Asia, Malaysia, Australia, Indonesia and the Pacific Islands, Africa, South America and even up into the Everglades of North America (maybe). Their epicenter seems to be New Guinea, Irian Jaya and the islands of Borneo, Indonesia, the Philippines, up through Malaysia and into Southeast Asia. Since they grow in many varied conditions it is impossible to cover them all, but there are several general ways of growing that will make them respond better and give you more flowers.

This book is an attempt to give those who have an interest in growing bulbophyllums a guide to their needs.

Please remember that many other people all over the world grow them superbly using very different methods, so this book is not meant to suggest that this is the only way to grow them, just the way I have learned to grow them.[1]

And I have grown them for over forty years and seen them growing in: Borneo, Malaysia, Thailand, Brazil, China, Nepal, India, the Philippines, various Botanic Gardens from Great to Graveside and most important, "in captivity".

I stumbled along growing them with many other orchids, and their sheer determination to live seemed to give them the upper hand when it came to being subjected to the sporadic and sometimes lethal ministrations coming from their captor, me.

I was basically well meaning and consciously tortured them only as a last resort to attempt to squeeze a bloom out of the ungrateful, stubborn, rambling, miserable little... (cue the oriental music)…

look deep within yourself grasshopper,
are you at your best when you are troubled, sick or hungry?
Could YOU produce a flower from nothing?

But grandfather, I need to produce a flower like a fish needs a bicycle –

---WHACK!!---

sorry, sir, Kum-Ba-Ya.

---

1 This makes me appear less like a know-it-all, even if I might be.

Ah, grasshopper, it appears you have been neglecting World Studies
as much as Third Eye 101,
Kum-Ba-Ya is African and we are in Asia.

Sorry, Grandfather

Anyway, back to the torturing...

After seeing a program about plants living in extreme desert conditions on one of those wonderful channels where you're shown how nature can ruin your day before you can find the remote, I had a thought...

After I finished the sandwich and the nap I went out to water my plants. They mostly didn't need it, but when a hose-a-holic needs to water, water happens. Anyway, while watering, I was remembering the program showing the devastation of a flash flood in the desert. One of the side comments to the story was the extraordinary amount of blooms on the desert plants that hadn't had any water for over FIVE YEARS. I thought how my plants would react to no water for that long and watered more heavily.

Then I thought about the conditions that existed in the areas from where the plants that I grew came[2].

Most of the plants that I grew in the bulbophyllum complex, {Bulbophyllum, Cirrhopetalum (**seer**'- oh - **pet**'- ah – lum), Trias (**tree**'- os) and their hybrids}, came from Asia through Indonesia to Borneo and Australia. These areas have very diverse habitats, but many of the plants

available for sale

came from similar overall climatic conditions, namely,

IT'S WET FOR A LONG TIME FOLLOWED
BY A FAIRLY DISTINCT DRY SPELL.

Whether getting water from rains that come every day for months on end, or growing along rivers, waterfalls or just above tidal ranges, or growing in damp, humid pockets near water in the forest, many of the bulbophyllums thrive where it is wet.

It seemed that an environment like that would be easy to duplicate.

However, this is not as easy as it seems. You can't throw your plants in a bucket of water and come back next week to see if they are all okay. They need an almost continuous supply of fresh water to thrive, and you will soon see how they grow when they thrive.

---

2   It took a while to construct that sentence without ending in a preposition.

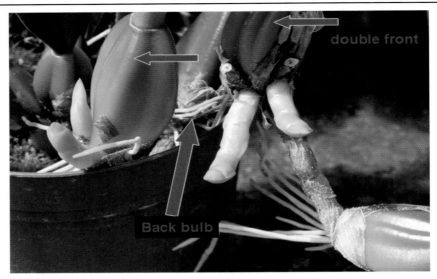

Here is where it starts. The bulb in the center at the top produced 2 bulbs (a double-front). From these I got 3 spikes (you can see 2 trimmed stubs on the bulb on the upper right). Then the bulb that gave me 2 spikes grew a new bulb (lower right), and now the previous year's bulbs are double-fronting so I have gotten 5 bulbs so far.

Several years later, the plant is out-growing a 12" saucer I use for the larger plants. If the plant is spectacular, I step it up into a basket (shown later). Divisions can be removed at any time depending on requirements. Keeping a plant large like this allows it to grow quickly and divisions can be taken often. If it is cut into 25-50 plants, they are all small and grow bigger much more slowly.

AOS Award slide; no photographer listed
Bulb. putidum 'Bill Sr.' CCM   84 pts
This was my first Cultural Award, given in 1978, and really encouraged
me to try to produce the biggest, nicest, best-flowered plants I could.

©Lewis Ellsworth
Bulb. lepidum 'D&B 42' CCM   91 pts
This is correctly named: *flabellum-veneris* (J. Konig) Aver.
We started numbering our Cultural Awards when we got to 25, unless it al-
ready had a clonal name or I wanted to name it something else.

©Thomas McGuigan

Bulb. Cindy Dukes 'D&B' AM-CCM   82 - 85 pts
(*rothschildianum X putidum*)
Named after Dorie's daughter.

©Don Wilson

Bulb. cocoinum 'D&B 25' CCM 84 pts

©Ernest Walters

Bulb. Icicles 'A-doribil Route 66' AM-CCM-CCE 86 - 85 - 93 pts
(*longissimum X wightii*)
This cross was made by Marilyn LeDoux of Windy Hill Orchids.

©Donald Wilson

***Bulb. rothschildianum* 'A-doribil' FCC-CCM-CCE   91 - 89 - 95 pts**
I took this plant to Mr. Wilson (and Polly and Karen) the day after
it received its 2nd award because it was obvious the show
photographer was unprepared for a plant this size.

Bulb. lobbii 'Kathy's Gold' AM/AOS
This plant never went to judging because I was busy using it for breeding.

©Monroe Kokin

Bulb. lobbii 'Bill's Bronze' CCM   88 pts
This plant I grew from seed and while it had 75 flowers, it only got 88 pts
because it was a small plant. It has gotten bigger.

©Lewis Ellsworth

Bulb. lasiochilum 'D&B 31 CCM   90 pts
The sad story of this plant is discussed later.

© Donald Wilson

Bulb. fascinator 'Hilltop' CHM-CCM-CCM   84 - 83 - 88 pts

©James Clarkson

Bulb. Frank Smith 'The King' CCE 96 pts
(*carunculatum X lobbii*)

©George Schudel

Trias picta 'D&B 27' AM-CCM-CCM   85 - 88 - 90 pts

Chapter 3
W = WATER

W A F L - H S* Growing Style

* Pronounced, waffle house after that great roadside food emporium.

I started an experiment in 1992. I took two divisions of a plant of *B. lasiochilum* that I was getting ready to pot up. Each one had about 15 bulbs. I mounted one of them on a piece of cork about eight inches long and two inches in diameter, a little block. The other one I put in a shallow plastic pot with a mix that stayed wet but open. At the time it only had a little sphagnum (sfag' – num) in it along with other stuff and we'll discuss sphagnum later on. Four years later, the one that I mounted on the piece of cork now was a little ball around this cork block with about 20 bulbs on it. The other was stepped up into a 6 inch by 12 inch basket and is much bigger as you can see in the picture of the two of them.

The one that I put into the wooden basket has received a CCM of ninety points. Here is the description:
87 flowers and 48 buds on 87 inflorescences (should say 135 inflr.); a virtually unblemished oblong plant 37 cm X 47 cm grown in sphagnum overflowing a wood and wire 16 cm X 30 cm shallow basket.

©Lewis Ellsworth

Bulb. lasiochilum 'D&B 31' CCM 90 pts

It received the ninety point CCM before I put it in its newest basket which
was 14 inches by 18 inches and grew for several years.
Then the plant got a rhizome fungus and by the time
I noticed it (my fault), the plant looked like this:

I counted the bulbs and the one on the cork has 40 and the larger plant HAD
1000. That's 25 times as big! Both started out the same size, remember.

Those are the results of a fork in the road, where one road gives you just the amount of water that you would get when getting watered with a hose as you walk by, and the other gives you a lot more. When you water like the first road, the plant begins to dry out as soon as you stop watering. If the plant takes in water slowly, it doesn't have much available to it. If it's mounted on something that dries out quickly, such as cork or hardwood, it doesn't stand a chance of reaching its true potential. The only hope is that the light is so low that it stays wet longer, but then you don't get the flowering you might.

The other road at the fork gives you water available for long periods of time and you can see the difference.

One of them is a standard-size plant like I used to grow and most people grow now. The other one is the kind I **now** grow over and over again for almost every kind of Bulbophyllum (or other genus) I've got. **And you can too!!**

Except, of course when it doesn't work and I kill the uncooperative, disloyal, unappreciative wretch of a plant, which probably had some incurable problem when I first got it, since it couldn't POSSIBLY be anything I did wrong.

(cue the music again)

We'll just concentrate on the good things in life, the magnificence and interconnectedness of all things and, of course, the supremacy of the orchid world and those who study it. Now let's all group-hug and sing Kum-Ba-Ya.

Speaking of Africa, many bulbophyllums from Africa and Madagascar go through a long dry spell that I am unable to duplicate due to my need to water. They have very interesting inflorescence shapes and flower over a long period of time. They seem to require a prolonged dry spell in order to initiate blooming and I can't let them get that dried-up looking before I have to water. Otherwise, it doesn't matter what I start with, in no time at all as you can see in the photos, I end up with a giant plant. There are a lot of different ways to grow large plants but as long as you have a nice plant at the end it doesn't matter how you got there. This is the opposite of the adage, "it's not the destination, it's the journey". In this instance, it **IS** the destination, not the journey. The main thing you are trying to achieve is to provide fresh water to them for longer periods of time.

The "bulb" part of an orchid is there because is has adapted to periods of dryness by storing water. How long and how severe that period is will determine how the plant reacts. If the plant grows in bright light, the leaf will be thicker or rounder or both, (i.e. *Bulb. rupicola*, Barb. Rodr.). Many times these plants will have CAM cells (Crassulacean Acid Metabolizers), which are designed to take in water at night. If the plant grows in shadier conditions, it will have a broader, softer leaf, (i.e. *Bulb. sumatranum*, Garay, et al. or *B. lobbii*). If the drying conditions are quite pronounced, you will get a plant that goes deciduous, (i.e. *Bulb. hirtum*, Lindl. or *B. comosum* Collett & Hemsl.). If you look at the back part of the plant, you can USUALLY tell something about its requirements. Just because it has no leaves on the back bulbs doesn't mean it wants to be dry. It may just be stressed. If the leaves drop in the fall with cooler, dryer air that USUALLY is a sign they go dormant. The nobile section of Dendrobiums is a good indicator of when to start reducing the water. Generally, the harder the leaf, the brighter the light.

LIES TO TOURISTS

The Tampa, Florida area where I have grown for 35 years has a diverse climate (yearly weather, egg-frying hot for months - with the added thrill of being in an ant, slug and roach-filled sauna, followed by periodic freezes for a few hours and back up the next day to world-class melanomic brightness)[3].

The way I adapt my growing style under these conditions is this way:

I pot up the plants primarily in shallow plastic pots. They are shallow because the plant's roots don't go very deep, they are not very large and the shallow but wide pots allow them room to grow. It's almost a problem now because the growth that I get is so pronounced in all directions that a plant that's outgrowing a two-inch pot can get stepped up into a five-inch bulb pan. Six to ten months later, it's outgrowing that five-inch bulb pan and needs to go into about a seven-inch pot. In a year-and-a-half from there it goes into a fourteen to sixteen-inch wooden basket. When you have hundreds and hundreds of plants and they are all growing that way, very quickly your space can be used up. But that's a problem that we should all have and I'll show you how to deal with that. I use Styrofoam peanuts as drainage and fill the rest of the pot with moistened Chilean (or New Zealand) sphagnum moss and pack it pretty tightly. I like the moss since it stays wet for a long time, is gentle on the plant's roots and bulbs, lasts for a long time and won't fall out if the plant tips over.

Remember, <u>the plants take in water slowly</u>, and if they don't have water available for a long period of time they will only grow a few

---

3   The previous weather report was entirely made up for comic relief and in no way bears any resemblance to the REAL weather in the Tampa Bay Region which is, of course, 72 degrees year round with a light breeze. The fun and exotic things flying by such as trees or sharks are only there temporarily for your enjoyment. Also, there is **probably** no truth to the urban-myth rumor that the Florida mosquito works for the government and returns a little blood from each bitten person to labs in the Everglades and Tallahassee that goes into a giant DNA database to be used to identify the descendants of the Roswell alien that escaped.

small bulbs during a season. At the end of that season, if they flower, the flowers will take a tremendous amount of water out of the bulb, so the bulb will become tiny and shriveled. Then, the next season when it's time to grow, it will only grow one bulb. I found this to be the case for hundreds of species and hybrids.

As it turned out, I happened to like watering and I water a lot. Consequently the things that were hung in the air did as well as they possibly could because they got watered at least every day and sometimes more often. After realizing that the plants take in water slowly and trying to figure out how to make the water available to them longer, I thought, hecky-darn, other plants that grow in dirt and dry out quickly can have a tray of water underneath them and the tray of water helps to keep them wetter longer, so WHY not try that with my bulbos?

I'd heard for years that you couldn't do this with orchids because it cuts off the air to their roots, they get a root fungus, which invades the rhizome, and you lose the plant over a period of weeks or months. {This can be true; the fungus is either a *Rhizoctonia* (rye–zok–**tone'**–ee–ya) species or a *Fusarium* (fyoo-**sare'**-ee-um) species}. However, if the depth of the water is **only** a quarter inch (5-6mm) or so, this **NEVER** seems to happen. I think the shallow tray is the difference between taking in water through a straw and sticking your whole head in a bucket. One will give you lots of water, the other will drown you.

If I had just a little shallow tray, like an inexpensive, aluminum oven liner that I purchased at the grocery store, I could give the plants water for several hours or up to a day more and not rot the roots. It was easy to find several candidates for this experiment and I set them in the shallow tray and watered them. When I was done, I figured the little bit of extra water would stay around for a day before it dried out. But guess what? 9It didn't. It was sucked up by the plants within the next four or five hours. Imagine that!. Who knew? So, I found I could give them fresh water that was available for many hours and still not rot the plants. What happened next was: the bulbs got fatter and plumper, the back bulbs slowly began to swell up and I started getting multiple fronts (a bulb would produce two fronts, or branch and then grow two bulbs from each branch). I also got back bulbs to produce new growths.

I began to see over a period of time that many things happened. If you could speed up six months like time-lapse photography, you would see the bulbs swell up and new growth burst out all over the plants. Now instead of just growing in one direction with one bulb, one time, and having the back die off like an inchworm, I now have two bulbs out of the front and two or three down along the side, like a starfish. The plant with only a little water has one bulb; the other has five to 10.

Six more months down the road, the plant that only got a little bit of water was still struggling with its one small bulb, and the plant that got lots of water for a long time, was now into the second bulbs from the front growth that had put out two growths, and each growth had matured into a full bulb and was now producing another growth out of that. Some of THEM were double fronting as well. So, those two bulbs became five but there are actually seven bulbs that have been produced - in one season, just out of the front - plus - the side bulbs each produced two, so that gave me four more. That made eleven on one plant against one bulb on the other the first year, thirty-five against one the second year. And so on, and so on, and so on. In a couple of years, I realized that most all of the bulbophyllums reacted that same way. Giant bulb plants (like *B. phalaenopsis* J.J. Sm.) don't do this as quickly since they put a lot more into each growth. They do grow faster if they get more food and water, just like all plants.

If you look a plant, and it's got shriveled old bulbs, and you stick it in a shallow tray of water, with a mix that is open and airy and yet holds water (especially good quality sphagnum), it will wick that water up and you will see the plant swell up and produce growths that come out everywhere, --- and --- you get much better results and much bigger growths. Since the plants are healthier, when it comes time to flower, you can imagine how much better they do. That was beneficial to plants that were newly imported, freshly bought, or weren't doing their best for whatever reason, as well. The plant that has only gotten a little bit of water has grown one bulb and at the end of the year, produced maybe one flower (usually none). The plant that has had all the water it wanted has produced somewhere between seven and fifteen bulbs and has a lot more plant behind it. Which one do you think is going to give more flowers, and bigger, better flowers, and longer lasting flowers? I even will say that the flowers have a richer color when the plants are in better shape and they are healthier.

TRUE STORY

I had a *B. lobbii* that produced a flower that had a pale yellow or cream color. Later on, when the plant was robust and healthy, and very, very strong, the flowers were much closer to peach or apricot and the reds and stripes came out more. Part of that has to do with fertilizer, and amount of sunlight, and the food that they are getting just before they flower, and temperature is known to affect flower color, I know, give me a break, it could be anything including sunspots, but I believe a certain amount of it has to do with how robust and vigorous the plants are, and you get that by having more water, longer. That's my theory. You're welcome to make up your own.

There is going to be a surprise quiz during this chapter, so pay attention!!!

If you want your plants to grow their best, you have to water thoroughly. That means you have to get them completely wet so they will stay wet as long as possible. That means you have to **WATER ALL SIDES**. If you don't water the other side, it won't get wet. If it doesn't get wet, the roots won't grow to that spot.

Try your own experiment at home.

You should be sure to have adult supervision, a note from your doctor and a properly charged cellular phone in case you need to call for assistance. Always wear head and hair protection, eye protection, ear protection, gloves, boots, a mask and heavy apron tied in back. Really, because, as your mother always said... you never know.

Take a slab of tree fern fiber, hold it horizontally and pour as much water through it as you want. Stay there and water it all day. No, really. Water to your heart's content but within the water-conservation guidelines of your local area. Now turn the slab over and look at the other side. Now you know the answer to the first question in the surprise quiz at the end of the chapter;

Do you water one side, or ALL SIDES?

If you answered ALL SIDES! you are now in the top 50 percentile of your class.

For bonus points in the surprise quiz we will have at the end of the chapter, answer,
What is the best way to water thoroughly?
and that is to,

use a wand about 18" to 2 feet long (45–60cm) with an angle at the end.

Add a brass shut-off valve at one end so you can turn off the water and pull that small weed while it is small, or adjust that plant to keep the flower spike from getting tangled before it is too late.

Add some kind of water diffuser at the other end and you are ready to go forth and do battle with the forces of dryness. If you get a mister nozzle that puts a small amount of water on the plant and a lot in the air, you can learn a lot about how mounted or hanging plants take in water. (Called a FOGG IT® nozzle but, trust me, pronounce it carefully when asking for one at the store). As you get closer to the plant while using the nozzle, you can really see how the plants get wet. You can see how the water rolls off at first, and slowly the dry areas begin to absorb water and transfer it to the center. If you START AT THE BOTTOM and mist upward, the plant is coated with a thin layer of water. Then as you water from the top and sides, this layer will act as glue for more of the water to be retained on the plant (called Hydrogen Bonding). More water gets into the growing medium or mount faster, and less goes on the ground, or your shoes.

Water <u>quality</u> is also very important.[4] Rain water is often good water and reverse osmosis water starts off with almost no impurities. A simple test kit to tell you the ph of your water will help you to tell if it is necessary to add anything to it to make it compatible with your food. Water that has a ph that is too high or too low (from the ideal of 7) will not mix with most plant foods. A conductivity meter will also help you tell the amount of dissolved solids in the water, so you can determine what must be done to achieve the best results.

There are many books written on water and what to do to change it. I recommend checking at your local library and reading one to get a better understanding of these things.

It isn't absolutely critical to know all these things. Just consider how many good growers there are who have no idea what their conditions are or what is happening with their plants. Most of the time it is just pure dumb luck (I speak from personal experience). But, if you really want to know about how to get the most from your efforts, you need to know the whole story. You can't balance your checkbook if you don't know the starting amount.

---

4   Talk to Courtney Hackney in North Carolina

**A mister won't miss 'er and Sir Sere will surcease!
Corny, huh?**

So, question 1: do you water one side or ALL SIDES?

That's right, ALL SIDES.

Bonus points – How do you get to ALL SIDES the best?

That's right; use a wand with a bent end and a brass on/off valve.

And finally, how do you water ALL SIDES THE MOST THOROUGHLY WITH THE LEAST WATER?

That's great – BOTTOMS UP!

TOP 50 PERCENTILE[5] WITH BONUS POINTS!

If the plant is growing on a mount, especially tree fern fiber or other porous material, the mount will hold water longer if it is horizontal rather than vertical. In fact, it could hold up to four times as much[6].

Try your own experiment at home (see PREVIOUS WARNING); after wetting a slab of tree fern or other porous material thoroughly, hold it horizontally until it stops dripping water. Turn it to vertical, hold it over your lap and watch what happens. Just kidding, don't watch. All the extra water that drips off could be kept in the mount and out of your lap if you keep the mount horizontal.

If the mount is horizontal AND in a shallow tray, you can imagine how fast it will rot, decompose and turn into a science project just killing my poor plant and why, oh, why did I ever listen to your cock-a-mamie ideas about watering?

No wait. That was just a relapse to previous fears. Everything will be fine. It won't rot if it dries out every few days. Sit down, relax, have a few Oreos[7]. Take deep breaths and repeat: It only hurts when I laugh, HA HA.

---

5   Thanks to Joe and Kathy Parker in California for explaining the difference between percent and percentile

6   Who knows, it could be more, I'm guessing

7   America's Favorite Cookie

Chapter 4
A = AIR

The next topic on our wafl-hs tour is AIR.

Many bulbophyllums have a bad reputation because a couple that are very common and easy to grow, have foul smelling flowers, [*B. putidum* (Teijsm. & Binn.) J.J.Sm., which is the correct name for the plants commonly called *B. appendiculatum* (Rolfe) J.J.Sm. or *B. ornatissimum* (Rchb.f.) J.J.Sm.; *B. echinolabium* J.J.Sm.; *B. helenae* J.J.Sm.; *B. levanae* Ames and *B. careyanum* Spreng. to name a few]. Many of them have no smell at all and several of them have a very, very pleasant smell. *B. emiliorum* Ames & Quisumb. smells like cloves, *B. laxiflorum* Lindl. has a minty odor and *B. propinquum* Kraenzl. smells like apples. Mostly, it was because the flowers either didn't last very long or seemed to be insignificant that they didn't gain more popular attention. The air is what gets the smell to your nose, but it also gets the plant growing processes going. Which means we need it and must have it in large quantities.

However, now it turns out that the bad things aren't as bad and the good things are much better and there are a lot of bulbophyllums that are out and available that are delightful and have long lasting flowers or flower over a long period of time, or have spectacular flowers produced only once a year like some Cattleyas, Dendrobiums, Paphiopedilums and other orchids. There are many, many good things in the Bulbophyllum genus and they are becoming more popular and that is as it should be.

Don't let anyone make you feel deranged or pathetic because you grow these. You are really a trend-setting visionary. Remember what they called Jacques Cousteau when he flew the first airplane, or what they called Lewis and Clark when they were lost in the northwest looking for a place to put their Louisiana Purchase. Remember what they called Tondalaya Schwartzkoff-Clepper after she married Throckmorton Blenchly-Phyfe-Sexton and insisted on becoming the first quadruple hyphenate.

What this has to do with air is remote at best so let's try to get back on track.

Deep breath, Oreo and Kum-Ba-Ya.

Air is no more important to your plants than to you. Maybe more. You can move if you don't like the air. Most plants don't have that luxury. You like fresh air, they like fresh air. You like fresh air day and night, they like fresh air day and night.

Imagine you are in a large plastic bag that is completely sealed. How long would you continue to be at your best if no one gave you any fresh air?

Without fresh air, your plants are using what little strength they have left to say uncomplimentary things to you regarding your lineage, sanity and of course, farmyard sexual proclivities.

Components in the air are used to complete chemical processes within the plants. Imagine the plant is a giant factory that makes various things through the year (new growth, leaves, flower stalks, flowers and finally, seeds). If the workers who come in for the second shift (the night) don't have the materials they need to build their stuff, the production on that shift doesn't occur. The factory across the street that makes sure the workers have everything they require will produce a lot more stuff and that translates into more flowers from more robust plants.

So, you need fresh air day and night to keep your plants at their best which helps them to cool down, get rid of old gases, dry off their leaf surfaces and have all the material they need to grow.

Here's the Surprise Test Question –

Would you rather have nasty old stale air that moves slower than that stingy friend reaching for the check,

or would you like to have fresh, moving air?

<u>GREAT!!</u>

fresh, moving air is right!!

Why? See two paragraphs above

NOW BONUS POINTS –

When is the most important time to have fresh, moving air?

AT NIGHT

Now you are in the top 25 percentile of your class. With Bonus Points! Keep it up. I'm proud of you.

<u>Most people don't realize the importance of the two things you just mastered.</u>

Chapter 5
F = FOOD

When the subject of fertilizers comes up, as it always does, the easiest answer to the question,

What is the best kind of food?
is:

ANY KIND OF FOOD

The plants can only get so much food from the decomposing media in or on which they are planted, and water they receive. If I gave you a choice of whatever food I offered, or none, you would quickly yearn for what little scraps you could get[8]. Plants are the same way, without all the complaining. So, any kind of food is better than no food at all. It is rare that you overdose a plant that hasn't been getting any food at all (especially if you follow label recommendations). And most fertilizers have something the plants can use.

INCHWORM GROWER

Most people are fooled into thinking plants are growing when they only water because the plants change shape. In reality, what is happening is the back of the plant is dwindling or dying and the mobile plant ingredients are being moved to the front. Often this is seen as back bulbs dropping leaves and shriveling or the loss of the lower leaves on vandas or phalaenopsis for each new leaf they grow. I call this Inchworm Growing.

STARFISH GROWER

In order to get your plant to grow bigger, you have to give it "FOOD" so it can use the "WATER" it has stored up to combine with the "FRESH AIR" it gets day and night to build more plant stuff. See how it all fits together? When you do this, the plants grow in all directions, branch in front and produce new growths from many back bulbs.
I call this Starfish Growing.

---

8 (See Steve McQueen in Papillon).

The plants take in a lot of water when they are in trays, so dilute the food. I have large areas of plants in water that isn't convenient to change, and I make sure the food is diluted so they don't burn. We will talk about when to feed later.

Some people use a "bloom boosting" fertilizer high in phosphorus hoping it will help to overcome a lack in other areas. I prefer to use a "Plant Encourager" which is high in nitrogen and potassium and low in phosphorus. I feel that a plant grown to the maximum will give you a lot more flowers than trying to chemically induce them from a poorly grown plant. That's another of my self-made theories. You are welcome to make up your own.

We make our own food because we can't get the same ingredients elsewhere. We call it Bill's Best™. It dissolves quickly and completely. It has no dye. It has a lot of nitrogen (for growth) in a form that is easy to absorb, as well as potassium that helps facilitate many other chemical processes. It has trace minerals as well. The trick with food high in nitrogen is to get the new growth to harden quickly so the tissues aren't as tasty to bugs and susceptible to pathogens (that's one of the Secret Ingredients). Also, most food has nitrogen in the form of **nitrite**. Oddly enough, the orchids mostly take in **nitrate** which is different. My food has nitrates so it is more betterer.

Since food is expensive and the medium is very porous, we water the plants first before feeding. There are some who feel that fertilizer on dry roots and leaves is beneficial, citing studies to that effect. If all you grow are vandaceous plants, this might be okay. I feel that the bulbophyllums take in water for hours. Therefore, if the water had food in it, they could take that in as well. Indeed, if the fertilizer isn't diluted, it can be too harsh. You should see the growth you get when you feed in the evening with a mild solution, which they take in for hours. Did I mention that we just got our 70th Cultural award (mid-2009)? Did I mention that they are in 25 different genera? Probably not, since I don't like to sing my own praises oo much. Did I mention that I am the most humble person you will ever meet?

We get our food to go much farther by watering first and coming right back and then feeding. What happens is that we get much more thorough coverage since the media and plants are wet, and we can use much less fertilizer since it isn't landing on the ground. Half as much food is giving us twice as much growth since it stays around much longer.

We started using ProTekt® (which is silicon) as a plant strengthener during hot and cold temperatures. It also seems to keep some fungus and insect problems down. We add it to the food once a month or so. Read and follow label directions.

So, here is your QUESTION;

What is the best kind of food?

ANY KIND OF FOOD

BONUS POINTS:

How do you get your food to go four times farther?

Water First And Use Half As Much

DOUBLE BONUS:

What is the VERY best kind of food?

Of course,
BILL'S BEST ☺

Well, you are three for three. Fantastic! You are zooming past the laggards and now are in the

TOP 12 PERCENTILE

Chapter 6
L = LIGHT

They don't have to grow in the dark.

Most growers have limited space to grow their plants, and with the addiction of orchids becoming stronger and stronger, space becomes more and more precious. Here are some things I have learned to do to get the most out of the least space and have **all** the plants get **all** the BRIGHT SHADE and FRESH AIR they need.

Aluminet on clear greenhouse

First, the greenhouse is covered with Aluminet®, which is silver colored plastic shading that reflects the sun and keeps the inside cooler, but still bright. This photo shows the greenhouse in the summer. I have a bottom layer of 50% shade that stays on all year long as well as a top layer of 30% that I put on about mid-April (in the Tampa Bay area) and remove about mid-October. The top layer is only on the top of the greenhouse because the light isn't as intense in the morning and we have large oak trees on the west side. If the trees weren't there, I would bring the cloth down the west side as well. The two layers don't add up to 80% shade even though the numbers do. The actual shade is about 65% and this keeps things from getting too bright and hot in our summers.

Inside the house, you are looking at the evaporative cooler on the north wall and the benches. The exhaust fans are behind me. This set-up pulls in fresh air which is cooled and moistened, and then sends it out to be replaced with more fresh air. The overhead fans come on when the exhaust fans shut down. I want the temperature to stay in the low 80s.

When I set the thermostats at 80°, the greenhouse always got into the 90s. I realized that by the time the air temp got up to 80°, the plants had absorbed too much heat to cool off with a little air movement. When I lowered the thermostat to 73° for the first fan and 76° for the second, the plants didn't get as hot. There is a big difference between not getting hot and cooling down. I use black ground cover on the floor which keeps weeds from growing and bugs from coming up from below. I have concrete pavers as walkways which keeps your feet dry as you water. I found that very quickly the ground in the aisles gets packed down and all the water runs to the aisles and you wind up standing in the water, which can be unpleasant. I also have a concrete block perimeter wall which keeps ALL insects from gaining an entrance at ground level. This wasn't always the way the greenhouses looked. Over 40 years I have learned (thanks to Dorie's incessant bitc – er, guidance) that the cleaner the growing environment, the easier it is to get the most out of your plants. You will find that stacks of pots or, worse, cardboard boxes of supplies in your growing area is a sure-fire way to give homes to bugs which will make you sad in a number of ways.

Now for the benches. This design (previous page) allows for the most number of plants in the smallest space. The top shelf is about 2 feet above the bottom and 2 feet wide. This allows you to reach the plants without too much effort and see everything clearly. We started with wood benches because that was what I saw at most of the other growers. When algae grew on the wood, it could be cleaned off with a power sprayer and at first looked great. However, I found that the sprayer "feathered" the edges of the wood and the algae grew back in no time. Now I make the benches out of the same kind of aluminum from which your patios are constructed. I bought a special saw that allows me to make precise cuts (called a "chop saw") and I got an aluminum-cutting blade and I was in business. It took a while to become a master bench maker, but now that I have done it for a long time, it is much easier. You can too. Never think you are too old or too stupid to learn something new. Look at me and you will see that anything is possible. "Measure twice, cut once."

Having a lip on the edge of your tables will give you a lot more room for plants. You knock the plants off as you walk by so it is natural to push them back away from the edge, which wastes the space that could be used.

This shows how the plants can be placed right up to the edge without fear of knocking them off. The wire troughs attached to the top shelf give you more growing space and a place to put the smaller plants or things in bloom you want to view.

Here is a shot showing how to get the most out of your space and still allow everything to get good light and air. Plants that like bright light are down under the benches.

Just kidding!

The lower the plant, the darker the light, so place plants according to their requirements. You are looking south and the exhaust fan (one of two) is on and running. The reason for setting up the house this way is because the sun goes south in the winter and if you had the evaporative cooler on the south end, it would shade a lot of plants all winter which you don't want. Having the cooler on the north side puts it in the shade which helps to keep it cooler which you want. We also shade the area OUTSIDE the cooler so the air ENTERING the cooler is as cool as possible which helps keep it cooler as well.

This is on the other side of the bench in the last picture and shows how it is possible to get an extremely large amount of plants in a small area and still have them do well. My half of the 18 X 24 foot greenhouse is 12 X 18 with 3 aisles. In 2008, I received 30 awards for my bulbos and they all came out of this area. I also have compots and seedlings here as well, so it is possible to grow world-class plants in this manner.

This is the table on the other side of the aisle. Plants in the center of the bottom layer don't rot from water dripping from above. Why? Because. Really, the good air circulation keeps the water from sitting on their leaves for too long, even when the plants are wet at night which we will discuss later.

The small fan in the upper left comes on at night for 15 minutes each hour to bring in fresh night air, which is essential for optimum growth, remember? It comes on year round (except on the nights it will get below 55 which is when the heaters come on). You can adjust yours to the heater temp in your area. You don't want the heater and exhaust fan to be fighting each other.

Many times the places the bulbophyllums grow are really much brighter than you would imagine and, provided that the plants don't get too hot from the sun, they can be grown as bright as possible - short of burning. However, with more sunlight, that means more water, and to a certain degree, more food. We grow in Florida. It's very bright. As mentioned before, our greenhouses are clear polycarbonate with aluminum colored shading on top of that stretched **above** the greenhouse. It keeps it shaded but very cool. We have an evaporative cooler and big exhaust fans for good air circulation. The plants thrive and grow beautifully under those conditions and that's very helpful. There are certain plants that like it "out" where it's hotter, like catts, dens, epis (and phals in the shade) in the court-yard by the pool and there are certain plants that like it "in" where it's cooler. By cooler, outside it may be ninety-five to one hundred degrees in the summertime in Florida, with 90% relative humidity. Inside the greenhouse, the hottest tempera-ture is about eight-four and it's mostly closer to eighty, eighty-two. The plants do the best when they're cooler because they can take in food better, more slowly, and because they're not expending as much energy cooling their leaves from the heat and the sunlight. They can use the sunlight to the advantage of making plant materials so you get more growth, and later more flowers.

Speaking of flowers, want some?

So far we have learned how to water and why. Then we found out air was important and when it was needed. We added food to that because we want to be starfish growers, not inchworm growers. So we have nice, big plants, but no flow-ers. Why? The answer is not enough light. Sunlight is essential for good flower production, in addition to giving you stronger plants and fewer problems with fungi and bacteria.

In the woods where the plants start their lives, the seeds land all over the place. The only ones to germinate <u>and live</u> are in the shadier areas. This is fine in the wild when coming into bloom quickly isn't a factor, in fact it is a detriment since you need a strong, mature plant to hold a seed pod (or 10). So the plants grow in shady conditions for a long time (sometimes years). Then one day the large tree beside them shading the plants falls down from age, storm or some other reason and now the plants get a lot more light. Sometimes too much, but that's nature. The increased light brings the plants into bloom with an immense show of blooms. This isn't the way it happens all the time, but I hope you get the idea.

Now you have learned that the plants will grow well under conditions of good water, good, fresh air circulation and shade. The way to get good blooms is to have **BRIGHT SHADE**. The plants can take much higher light than you think (if they don't get too hot, have I said that enough?). Higher light will give you strong-er plants more resistant to problems and the most bestest thing of all, **BLOOMS!!**

In order to tell how much light you have, go out at the brightest time of day and wave your hand about 12 inches (30 cm) above the leaves of your plant with fingers spread apart. You can't go out at night with a flashlight since you don't get an accurate reading. If you can't see a shadow at the brightest time of day, open your eyes. If you still can't see a shadow, it's time for silk plants. If you can see a faint shadow, it's phalaenopsis time. If you can see a decent shadow, it's time to buy more bulbos.

If you hold the leaf with your hand for a few seconds and it is hot, it's too hot for good growth without burning[9].

We hope you're alive, which means that your hand is 99°. If the leaf is hot to your hand, it is hotter than 104° and the growth has shut down in favor of cooling the plant. It does this by transpiring, which means that it is using up its water to keep the leaves from burning. We perspire, they transpire (among other things). Same reasons. You can't always add water to the plant to make things better but it can help at times. Just making it windier by adding a fan doesn't always help unless the air blowing over the plant is cooler. Blowing hot air at the plant just dries it out faster. Sitting in shallow trays can help for a while, but the best thing is to lower the temperature. We use Aluminet© which is a mylar plastic shadecloth that is silver in color and reflects the light rather than just shading it down. We first ran across this product used by George and Jean Schudel, growing orchids south of Jacksonville, Florida, two delightful old coots who grow a variety of species and miniatures. Black shadecloth gets hot and transfers that heat into your growing area. The Aluminet® can be obtained from Imperial Builder's and Supply in Apopka, Florida (1-800-442-4147) among other places. We use a 50% bottom layer and add a 30% top layer in the summer which I remove about October in the Tampa Bay area of Florida. You have to adjust for your own particular growing conditions and climate. It really made a big difference in how much brighter I could grow the plants and still keep it cool. Thanks George and Jean!!

---

9   Except for Jim Clarkson in Tampa

<u>QUESTION TIME;</u>

How do you tell how much light you have?

Fingers spread apart to look for shadow

How do you tell if you have too much light?

Hold the leaf!!

BONUS POINTS

How do you keep your growing area cool and bright?

ALUMINET®

You are now in the top 6 Percentile of your class!!

Chapter 7
H = HOME

I found when growing BULBOS on tree fern fiber slabs and totems and balls and things like that over the years a couple of things happened:

One, after a number of years the plants were no longer able to grow on the tree fern fiber and wound up declining for no obvious reason. The reason was, the tree fern absorbed salts from fertilizers and minerals from water that were very difficult to get rid of,

And, two, depending on which way I had it hung, the amount of water obtained by the plant was affected greatly. I had always grown totems straight up and down, I had always seen them straight up and down, they stack or they can be hung up against a wall straight up and down and the lower ones get better light. That's the way I've always seen them. However, if you turn a totem sideways, or if you have a slab, flat, it will hold four times the amount of water.[10] As soon as I started turning the tree fern fiber slabs sideways or flat, the amount of water that they held went up tremendously. That meant the plants did much better because they had more water available to them longer.

So when you put things on tree fern fiber for the first time, you have to make sure to water all sides carefully, and thoroughly, and fully. Otherwise, it won't get wet and the roots won't grow where it's dry. By putting a plant on tree fern fiber positioned sideways, and then lying it down in a shallow tray for the first week or two after it's potted up, the tree fern fiber gets much wetter sooner. It absorbs water better and then when you hang it in the air you can get it more thoroughly wet. You can drill a hole at each corner and use the 4-way hangers that vanda growers use and it will keep the slab more stable for the life of the plant. (which will be until the salts build up and the roots die and the plant declines).

Really. I try to make this fun and easy, but the reality is that these simple things are the basics for all growing, and by understanding the importance of keeping them in balance, you gets better results from the time spent with your plants. This in turn rewards you by bringing you good feelings instead of stress.

That way you can avoid becoming a karmic-challenged lost heathen soul, gnashing your teeth while wailing and pouring decomposed orchid mix over your head, fighting off mechanical spiders from outer space and wandering from nursery to nursery begging others to take your money in exchange for their blooming plants that you then tell your friends you grew.

---

10 See previous guess on page 39.

For most orchids in pots and baskets, I mix large and medium fir bark, large and medium charcoal, coarse Spongerok®, (which is also called extra large Perlite®) and some kind of porous rock (Aliflor®, Lava Rock® or any one of many others). I NEVER use chopped cocoanut husks since they are salty to begin with and get worse as time goes by. Some growers use them and do fine (see Allen Black in Virginia). It is a basic mix and I add different things to it depending on what kind of orchid genus I'm going to grow (tree fern for phals, oyster shells for some paphs). I rinse all of these and I blend them together and that's my mix. We store the different mixes in large tubs we get from Home Depot that are sold for mixing concrete at home. They cost about $5 and work well. I have smaller bins I got at the Dollar store for … a dollar. I use these to hold a smaller amount of the mixes when I am potting. If you grasp the bin FIRMLY on each side and move it back and forth BRISKLY, you will see that the larger parts of the mix come to the top. If you slide them off to one side, you will see the smaller parts of the mix underneath. Now you have separated the mix into larger parts for use in the bottoms of pots and the smaller parts to use on top. Don't forget to suit up in your safety gear, because… you never know.

For my bulbos, now I use Chilean sphagnum moss as talked about earlier. The previous mix is tailored a little for the different genera such as Cattleyas, Dendrobiums and Encyclias. We add a little shredded tree fern fiber and seedling fir bark for Phalaenopsis.

Seedlings use seedling grades of the above and smaller pots.

<u>Building a Basket</u>

There are two ways of coming up with a basket of just the right depth. One is to reduce a standard basket down by uncurling the hanger wire rings at each corner and removing about two layers from each side, depending on the construction.
I want to wind up with a basket that has 4 slats on one side and 3 on the other.
Baskets are too deep for most orchids, except vandas, because they stay too wet and don't give the plant the right air around the roots. I know I've said the bulbos want more water longer, but they don't get the right amount of air/water growing in deep baskets or large, deep pots.

You can also make your own. I use cedar planks I get at Home Depot (also called HOPE DEPOT) and cut them into slats. I cut the slats to length (about 14-16 inches [35-40cm] by 18-20 inches [45-50cm]) and use ½ X ½ hardware cloth for the bottoms. I like the slats to be rectangular, not square since they look nicer this way. You can cut the hardware cloth with tin snips and I coordinate the length of the slats to fit the holes in the wire so it doesn't stick out. Neatness counts. Here is a plant in a 5 inch pot in the fall of 1998:

Bulb. rothschildianum 'A-doribil' **Fall, 1998**

©Don Wilson

Here is the same plant one year later with a 91 pt FCC/AOS and an 89 point Cultural Award

Two weeks later, I did this to it:

First, I assembled the slats I would need for the basket and made sure they all looked nice. Then I drilled holes in the ends of them all and the middles of the bottom two. As you can see, it's very simple. In the bottom photo, the black line allows me to drill all the holes in the slats at the same distance from the ends so the basket looks nice when finished. Neatness counts.

Next I get the bottom layer with the wire all positioned and the first layer of slats in. The middle bottom slat gets wired in now, since you can't do it later. You also have to wire the middles of the ends so they don't sag. U-shaped heavy wire is used at the corners to tighten up the slats and make the rings to attach the hanger.

Now I just stack the slats a layer at a time until it is done. I like to have 4 on the long side and 3 on the short. I know, it IS kind of neurotic but everyone needs a hobby.

Note that the bottom slat has been wired to prevent sagging. Now it is time to line the basket with sheet moss. This comes from the orchid suppliers and is used to cover pots and baskets for the shows. Sometimes, you can get leftovers from the vendors at the end of the show when they tear down. Here is how you use it after you wet it:

By taking a bamboo stake and using it as a probe, you can fill the openings in the sides. Push from the inside while the basket sits on a flat surface. After completing all sides, lay flat and cover the bottom. Placing sheet moss upside down will leave the pretty side facing out. Remember, neatness counts!

Now that we FINALLY have the basket ready, it's time to put in the plant.

Bulb. rothschildianum 'A-doribil' FCC/AOS out of water pan

I take all the old mix off the roots since it is almost always broken down, not to mention full of salts and minerals. Then I put a mound of Styrofoam peanuts in the middle. This is going to be the center of the basket. They last about 5 years. If they stay wetter, they rot sooner. If they are too dry, the plants don't grow well. By filling the center with light, non-porous material, you can provide a nice, wet world for years and **that is the secret.**

With the plant all cleaned off, it is ready to be positioned in the basket. It's your own happy little world, so you can do anything you want. The rhizomes are fairly pliable so you can do a good deal of arranging.
I set the basket up on pots so I can push wires curled over the rhizomes through to the bottom and twist them to keep the plant firmly in place. This holds the rhizomes securely, but be careful not to break them.

Now **ADD MORE** Styrofoam under the rhizomes and around the roots. This is an **important step** to make the plant secure for a long time.

Once the plant is secure, it is time to put in the medium. I used to use the bark mix but now I use Chilean sphagnum moss. I work it entirely around the plant and into all the cracks and crevasses. You can lift the front bulbs a little and fit a little more around the roots. I pack it tightly. When you are done, it should look something like this:

You don't want to leave it like that so here is how you finish it up. Take nice pieces of sheet moss and place them fancy side up around the bases of the bulbs. You can lift the bulbs to get the moss to fit better. Also, it is possible to fit small pieces in the center and cover the medium. Trim all old spikes and clean the leaves. Add a nice tag with all the info you want. I use aluminum tags for special plants since they don't get brittle and if you press hard with your marker, the letters are em-bossed into the tag and you don't have to worry about it fading. Also, if you wire the tag on the hanger, basket or plant, they never get removed by birds, squirrels or careless friends. The finished product looks like this:

Notice how the hanger wire has been crimped around the ring. This keeps it from coming loose or rattling. The next photo shows the old pot and the final results.

And this is what it looked like 14 months later (3-01):

And this is what it looked like 7 months after that (10-01):

©Donald Wilson

Bulb. rothschildianum 'A-doribil' FCC-CCM-CCE/AOS

This concept works for large pots as well. Just make sure you have a large amount of Styrofoam in the center since that is the wet zone.

You are also going to have to think about what kind of mount to put a plant on. Many times wood has a fibrous mass or bark; cypress or cedar are some of the best that are available in the Florida area, but it's best to find something that is more locally available rather than something that comes from halfway around the world. Having something locally available is much better to adapt the plants to and you don't have to worry about the shipping charges because it is local. You can use nylon line, strips of old panty hose, telephone wire, string, just about anything at all bearing in mind that the wire is hard and you don't want to break through the rhizome or the roots. You just want to attach the plant and give it an opportunity to grow onto whatever it is that you are using as a mount, whether it's tree fern fiber, or some wood product, or some synthetic, spongy products that are designed in totems or who knows, you might even buy some animal shaped topiary base or something and allow a vining plant to grow on the outside of it. Any number of things can be imagined but the most important thing is that you want to provide a nice home for the plants.

Chapter 8
S = SICKNESS

PESTS AND DISEASES

Scales and mealy bugs don't seem to be quite as bad a problem with the bulbophyllums as some of the other orchids. *Bulb. medusae* (Lindl.) Rchb.f. will sometimes get scale, but I don't have too much trouble otherwise. With the plants hanging out in the open, roaches and crickets and things like those that can get to the tender roots and fresh flower spikes seem to be more of a problem than scale and mealy bugs. That requires the conscientious effort of cleaning your entire growing area.

One of the best reasons for having a green house, or a shade house, or a structure of some kind, where you separate inside from outside, is to be able to clean the inside and keep it as bug-reduced as possible. You can never keep them all away forever. It requires constantly patrolling and looking for new out-breaks. Ants are one of the first indicators of problems because they bring eggs and babies of problem insects to your plants.

GREAT IDEA!!

One very good way to be a Master Grower is to learn to be a great ob-server. If you are not already one now, (and most people aren't), you can teach yourself how.

Get a friend (and if you don't have a friend in the whole world I will teach you how to do this by yourself). Give your friend ten **OLD** pennies and have him or her put them on your plants randomly. Don't put them under the pots or down in the mix, but just on the top. It will be hard enough this way. Your job is to find the 10 pennies. Any you don't find means you owe your friend a dollar per penny. Now go over to your friend's growing area and repeat the procedure. Very quickly, you will see how different **REALLY** observing your plants is from what you have been doing, which was scanning. Looking for pennies is no different than looking for problems. When you teach yourself to be a better observer, your plants will not have the problems they now have since you will spot them long before they become big problems.

If you have no friends, you can take the pennies in your hand , stand with your back to your plants, and toss the pennies over your shoulder. You can't place your own pennies, since – if you can't find them after you placed them yourself -- you have much greater problems than poor observation.

With the advent of trays of water and having things much wetter, two other problems can show up. One of them is mollusks, in the form of slugs or snails. A lot of the time, the snail eggs will be in some media you get or in pieces of fir bark or something. You diligently try to keep the place clean and they still show up. You need to use various baits for slugs and snails. I have also used –

(insert standard disclaimer, "you use everything at your own risk"), equal parts of liquid Sevin®, honey, and molasses mixed up in just a small amount at a time; say a tablespoon of each in a jar with a wooden stick.

You can go around and you can paste this mixture on the sides of pots, or the insides of benches, or areas of table's legs, things like that or where you see the damage to plants.

With more moisture, you can have fungus and bacteria problems. That is why having shallow trays that dry out rapidly so you don't get a big algae build up is much better than having deep trays where the water stays around for a long time. Having the water dry out kills the bacteria off that may be growing and keeps it generally cleaner because it requires fresh water every couple of days. The best preventative of pathogens is **FRESH MOVING AIR AND BRIGHT SHADE**. Fungi must rest on the leaf for some time before they can grow in. If they are being blown along, they can't get a foothold, so-to-speak. They can get in through wounds so keep damaged parts removed and put cinnamon on open cuts to discourage entry.

Here is a list of the things I use and where I get them:

I'll start from the safest and work up from there.

As ALWAYS, read and follow label directions (where possible).

The least chance for plant injury occurs when chemicals are applied when it is

COOL.

This is what I use on MY plants.

USE THESE AT YOUR OWN RISK.

**AS ALWAYS, READ AND FOLLOW LABEL DIRECTIONS.
SPRAY WHEN IT IS COOL AND DON'T ALLOW DRIFT.
USE THE MILDEST CHEMICAL FIRST.
CHANGE FROM ONE TO ANOTHER IF POSSIBLE.
KEEP YOUR GROWING AREA CLEAN AND THE
PLANTS OFF THE GROUND AND WEED FREE!**

AOS PEST AND DISEASES (available from the American Orchid Society; AOS.org about $12) this comprehensive and handy book lists plant problems with good photos, how to fix, gives the chemical name and has a table of Brand Names. A must for every serious grower.

Pro-Tekt (available from Dyna-Gro 1-800-DYNAGRO [396-2476]) This strengthens the cells of plants and makes them resistant to stress from heat and cold and makes it hard for fungi and bacteria to enter plants. I like to apply it once a month or so, and I apply it by itself. It can be mixed with other foods, but not in concentrated forms.

NEEM OIL (Dyna-Gro) The best product for bugs and fungus. Made from the seeds of a tree from India, the waxy liquid smothers the insects or fungi. It has been used for 2000 years as a stomach and mouth healer and used for skin problems, so it is actually beneficial to get on you. Mix with hot water and Palmolive® Detergent to form yellow milk and apply to the plant. Very effective and insects can't become immune to it.

CINNAMON (Powder from Grocery store) Used for treating wet rot (bacteria). More than just drying the area, cinnamon seems to kill many kinds of bacteria so they don't return. Apply full strength to the affected area, set plant aside and don't water for a few days.

HYDROGEN PEROXIDE 3% (Grocery or Drug store) used for treating wet rot (bacteria). Not as good as cinnamon, but cheaper. Use full strength on affected area. Don't water for a few days.

ALCOHOL (Isopropyl rubbing 70%; Grocery or Drug store) Used for all insects. Apply full strength on insects (but not at noon since it evaporates too quickly). **Do <u>not</u> use on Paphiopedilum buds.**

DIATOMACEOUS EARTH (Pool Supply stores and Home Depot)
Used in pool filters. Crystalline remains of hard-shelled algae make a formidable barrier to insects. Either dissolve in water and pour as a barrier around your growing area, or broadcast dry. You must make a wide barrier because the insects need to crawl through it and get cut by the sharp edges. Any cuts will prove fatal. It also drys them out. Needs to be replenished often since it washes away. Not expensive (about $20 for 25 pounds).

Diatomaceous Earth Pest control (From Wikipedia)
Diatomite is also used as an insecticide, due to its physico-sorptive properties. The fine powder absorbs lipids from the waxy outer layer of insects' exoskeletons, causing them to dehydrate. Arthropods die as a result of the water pressure deficiency, based on Fick's law of diffusion. This also works against gastropods and is commonly employed in gardening to defeat slugs. However, since slugs inhabit humid environments, efficacy is very low. It is sometimes mixed with an attractant or other additives to increase its effectiveness. Medical-grade diatomite is sometimes used to de-worm both animals and humans. It is most commonly used in lieu of boric acid, and can be used to help control and eventually eliminate a cockroach infestation. This material has wide application for insect control in grain storage.

BORIC ACID (Garden Centers and Home Depot) Great for roaches
and other crawling insects. Interferes with their ability to digest food and they die. Also, is very drying to their bodies. Very safe for pets and people. Apply where they (the insects, not the pets and people) will come in contact with it (walk over it).

BACILLUS THURINGENSIS (Home Depot) Very mild bacteria
used to kill caterpillars and worms attacking plants and vegetables. Follow label directions. Not harmful to other insects.

LIQUID SEVIN (Ortho; available at Home Depot and Garden Centers)
Use this to make a paste for slugs and snails. Mix equal parts Sevin, Molasses and Honey. Put paste in jar with lid to keep fresh for several months. Apply with stiff tag or popsicle stick to piece of bark or inside edge of pot on plants being chewed. One tablespoon of

each ingredient will make plenty.

DEADLINE (Carterandholmes.com or Pestproducts.com) very effective for all mollusks. Apply this gray paste around plants being affected by slugs & snails and clean up dead bodies in the morning. Only use a little since it is messy. Hard on pets. If you have pets, use SLUGGO, also available from Pestproducts.com.

RAID HOUSE & GARDEN AEROSOL SPRAY If you can't find this at various stores, check SCJohnson.com and you may be able to order it directly from them. Used to hunt down roaches at night. Go out 2-3 hours after the sun goes down with a flashlight. You need to sneak up on them so they don't hide and spray JUST A LITTLE on them. Go to the plant with the obvious chew damage on flowers or leaves. They will be there or nearby. Spray is cold when it leaves the can so don't overdo it or you will freeze your plants. Also kills thrips, mealy bugs and scales.

ALL-IN-ONE ROSE SPRAY (Bayer; Home Depot) I use this in a spray bottle for spot spraying of plants and spraying of the roots since it is a systemic (taken up by the plant and sent to the cells). It works against bugs and fungus, but I can't vouch for all types of or-chids since I primarily use it on Cattleyas, Encyclias and Catasetums. Mix as per label directions.

ENSTAR II (Wholesale nursery chemical supply stores, hard to find, expensive) comes in a 5 ounce bottle for about $60. Interferes with the insect's ability to molt so they don't reach maturity and can't breed. Very effective against most insects which is why it costs a lot. Should be used as a last resort.

CATEGORIES OF PROBLEMS

Problems fall into five main categories: bugs, pathogens (fungus or bacte-ria), virus, environmental (sunburn, chemical burn, salt, buildup, etc.), or genetic.

You know you have bugs when you have plant parts leaving the plants without your help or you have a buildup of "stuff" on leaf surfaces. Most bugs come out late at night so if you go out and look at your plants with a flashlight at

11pm you will find what is eating them. It is possible to spray the insects you find with Raid House and Garden® Insect Spray which will not harm the plants.

Rubbing alcohol used full strength from a mister bottle will put the hurtin' on most insects providing you spray properly, and,

HOW DO YOU SPRAY PROPERLY?

The surprise question for this section is going to be, "when is it COOL to spray chemicals on your plants? The answer -- watch this -- is:

WHEN IT'S COOL!!

Pathogens are problems with the plants that stay right there, like black spots or mushy leaves. Fungus (plural, fungi [**fun**'-gye]) is dry and bacteria are wet.

To fix fungus problems, refer to the AOS book on Pests and Diseases®. Dusting fresh cuts with cinnamon will keep fungus from entering the plant at that point. Bacteria can be stopped using full strength Hydrogen Peroxide from the drug store (3%) or cinnamon powder. These are great for crown rot in vandas or phalaenopsis.

Environmental problems come in many forms.
Too much sun burns the leaves and bulbs. This can be fixed by putting the plants in a shadier spot.

Salt build-up occurs from a mix or growing slab that has absorbed too much of these salts. Salts are in all fertilizers (it can't be helped) and minerals are in much of the water you get from the city or your well. The less the better. Sooner or later it will build up to toxic levels. It is almost impossible to remove them once they are in the medium. If you want to try to flush them out, you must water thoroughly, **WAIT 20-30 MINUTES**, and then water again. It takes about that long for the salts to dissolve so they can be flushed out, if possible. If you don't wait long enough, the salts just recrystallize on your roots.

I have found that in Florida, the days get too hot too early to spray in the morning because even if you spray early when it is relatively cooler, it heats up right after you have sprayed and the plants can be harmed by chemicals that would be fine, -- if only it was cooler. So I spray in the late afternoon, or later. If the temperature stays down, it is probably better to have the plant surfaces dry out sooner than later, but I would rather have the spray around longer with cool conditions than gone more quickly but hotter. This avoids chemical burn.

Genetic problems show up periodically. Crosses between Encyclias and Cattleyas, for instance, often have spots on the leaf tips, I believe due to a genetic problem. This is cosmetic and if you can live with it, don't worry about it. If you bloom a plant several times and it has mutated flowers, throw it out. Life is too short to waste time and money on a plant giving you headaches. Likewise, any plant with a weird growth or flower that shows up consistently should be discarded. It is peculiar that so much time is spent caring for inferior, poor-growing plants that also seem to be vectors for insects and pathogens.

Finally, virus.
What to do? First, realize that it is impossible to keep your collection virus-free forever unless you have EVERY plant tested for EVERY virus before it enters your growing area and frequently after that, which is cost-prohibitive and tests don't exist for many of these viruses. If you keep your growing area as clean as possible, only use fresh razor blades or sterilize your tools between EACH plant, repot on newspaper that is changed between EACH plant, wear rubber gloves you change between EACH plant and wash your hands with Clorox between EACH plant, Clorox your tables at LEAST twice a year and only buy plants that are in tip-top shape, you might keep the virus levels down to a dull roar. I try to do most of the aforementioned, but I can't wash my hands in Clorox or wear rubber gloves because I hate them[11], so I don't worry about what I can't change (part of the serenity prayer). I have yet to see a bulbo that has obvious virus symptoms either in the growth or the flower, so I have convinced myself that it isn't a big problem. See how you can delude yourself if you try?

Here is a trick question;
Is fertilizer a chemical? The answer is YES!!

I try to feed my plants in the evening for two reasons; first, because chemicals are less injurious when it is cool and dark, and second, it lasts a lot longer so the plants get a lot more of it instead of its evaporating into the air and only leaving salt crystals on the roots to burn them. It works for me no matter what studies were done on vandas. I get significantly more growth feeding this way and have for 30 years. Dorie and I have recently received our 70th Cultural Award in over 27 genera (as of mid-2009) so I feel quite sure it works. 28 of those awards are in the Bulbophyllums (more than anyone else in the world), so it definitely works for them.

---

11   We have a nice but forceful, drill-sergeant-type lady named Lyla Shepard in the Tampa Orchid Club who was demonstrating how she works on her plants and when she snapped on those rubber gloves, something in me just cringed and puckered up so much that I now have a fear of gloves.

Chapter 9
Growing from seed

It is both easy and difficult to grow from seed. It is easy to make hybrids and send the pods to an established lab (if you can find one) and have them send you back flasks (you hope). It costs money for each bottle, but they do it for a living and are sometimes very good. It is more difficult to sow your own seeds and do your own flasking. The hard part is to avoid contamination of the bottles. Orchid seeds have no food around them (like a peanut) so they have to be given supplemental food (mostly sugars). Since fungi and bacteria grow on the sugar as well, the bottles have to be sterile and remain so for many months. There are several books on growing orchids from seed so I refer you to them for that part. I will show you how to make the cross and grow them out from the flask stage.

The first part of hybridizing is deciding which two plants to cross together. Or you can just cross whatever is open that day and spend years growing the plants until they bloom (if ever). Sometimes this works well, most of the time you are sorry.

I used to take the pollen out of the flower that was going to receive the new pollen since I was afraid that the plant could be pollinated with its own pollen. I now leave the pollen in because in that way, the flower stays fresh longer and the new pollen has a better chance to grow down the tubules into the ovary and make the cross. When the pollen is removed, the flower often will begin to senesce (sen - **ess'**), which means grow old and drop.

A quick lesson in terminology: using *B. lobbii* 'Kathy's Gold' AM/AOS as an example, if you took the pollen from 'Kathy's Gold' and put it back onto the same plant (or a division of the same plant), it would be called a "selfing". If you took pollen from a different clone of *B. lobbii* (say 'Bill's Bronze'), and made the cross either way (having either plant be the pod parent), you would have an "outcross". This is a better way to achieve greater gene diversity. If you took pollen from any other plant beside a *B. lobbii*, you would make a hybrid. A cross between two species is called a "primary hybrid". Beyond that it is called a complex hybrid. Crosses are named the same no matter which plant holds the pod.

When you make a hybrid that has not been registered before (all hybrids are registered at the Royal Horticultural Society in England), you can name it almost anything you want (within reason). Since there are over 2800 species of Bulbophyllums the possibilities are limitless. Go forth and multiply!

Here is how it's done:

Pollen on toothpick

Stigmatic surface
(where the pollen goes)

Lip removed

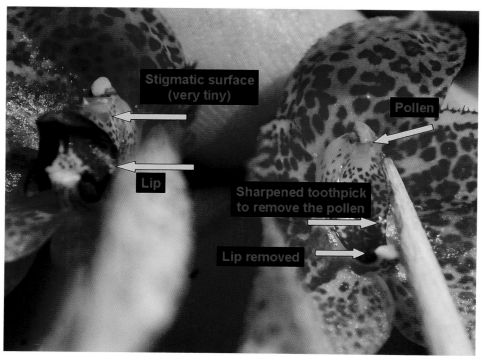

Stigmatic surface
(very tiny)

Pollen

Lip

Sharpened toothpick
to remove the pollen

Lip removed

Now, you have decided which plants to use and you have made the cross. What happens next?

For starters, you throw a big party, invite 500 of your closest friends and celebrate the imminent arrival of the newest and bestest hybrid since Abel or Cain or Arnold. Then you wait until the cross has produced a seed pod , the pod has matured, the seeds are fertile, the flasks don't contaminate, the plants make the transition to compots or flats, the seedlings grow big and strong... and finally... the cross flowers!!!

You now know the thrill of expectation and the agony of reality. Most crosses don't make it all the way to bloom and of the few which do, only a small percentage of those are great. That is one reason why I am very proud of the high number of my hybrids that have received awards (30 in all genera, 23 in bulbos as of mid-2009).

Anyway, enough about me and how wonderful I am. Let's focus on you. How do you feel about how wonderful I am? Just kidding. Since you are the most important thing in your life, you have a cross, what now?

First, the seed pod.

The pods can be small as with this cross using *B. frostii* Summerh.:

Or they can be large, as with this cross using *B. echinolabium* J.J.Sm.

Generally, I have found hybrids take about 4-6 months to mature while selfings and outcrossings take much longer. This doesn't always occur, but often enough so I keep my "eyes on the prize" around those times. If you are doing green pod work, you can harvest a little early and still get germination. If you are sowing dry seed (seed from pods that have opened), you just have to wait until the pod opens and hope you don't lose the seed to the wind. There is also the added worry about sterilizing the seed without killing it. Jim Clarkson gets grea germination with dry seed, but he doesn't accept new clients. Sorry, (snicker,snicker). Green pod work is usually better since the pod can be scrubbed with Clorox without damaging the seeds inside. Check the ads in the <u>AOS Bulletin</u> and the <u>Orchid Digest</u> magazines for firms that do flasking.

Now everything has gone just fine and you wind up with this:

A nice flask of 30-40 plants ready to come out. You can wrap the flask in newspaper and hit it with a hammer, or you can gently work the plants out without breaking the bottle so it can be reused. Either way, it's time to pot them up.

I use 4" plastic pots with medium mix as drainage (see previous chapters). On top I use a seedling mix consisting of: equal parts; seedling perlite, seedling charcoal, seedling fir bark and seedling tree fern fiber. I blend them all together and pot this way:

I fill the pot about half way with the medium mix and add a small layer of seedling mix to make the level even.

Then I place the individual plants around the outer edge leaning against the side. There are usually a few plants that will stand up by themselves and I put them in the middle (about three in a triangle).

Now I take the seedling mix in a handful and pour it around the plants in the middle. I have a thin metal stick (a piece of split bamboo works fine) and I place it against the outer plants and straighten them up while pouring the mix between the plant and the edge of the pot. I work my way around the pot until they are all upright.

Now here is the hard part and the secret. I place my hand over the plants in the pot lightly and, while holding them in place from moving too much, I tap the edge of the pot while moving around all sides. This settles the mix down around the plants, firms them in and makes everything more betterer.

I put about 12-15 plants in a pot and I keep them as close in size as is practical. When I'm done, it looks like this:

In about 8 months, they look like this:

If I don't get around to separating them out at this point, in another 8 months to a year, they look like this:

It is best to repot long before this point, but sometimes it isn't possible. Another reason orchids are so much fun to grow; they are so forgiving if you are busy, whether it's taking a much needed break, taking care of family or taking over a neighboring country. When you get back to them, they are usually still there and ready to grow.

When it's time to separate the seedlings, they go into individual pots, each according to its needs and they look something like this:

In a couple of years (more or less), the plants bloom and you are THRILLED!! Now, if it has never been registered, you can send the new name you have just given your cross -- off to the RHS -- pay the fee (currently about $16 US) and you have your very own cross, made by your very own hands and named by your very own mind.

© Ernest Walters

**B. A-doribil Super Star 'A-doribil Too' HCC/AOS
= B. (Stars And Stripes X *echinolabium*)**

**B. A-doribil Candy 'Frank's Favorite' AM-CCM
= B. (Elizabeth Ann X *bicolor*)**

Here is a progression of a single plant from compot to .... well, wait and see.

Here is the compot of Bulb. Doris Dukes from where the seedling came. The plant on the left is the one I picked.

Here is the seedling I chose and put into a 3" pot ready to come out (about 10 months later)

Here is the plant (also shown in Chapter 2) repotted into a 6" bulb pan. After blooming and showing great potential, I decided to repot at the optimum times to get the most out of its growth.

Here is the plant 18 months later in a 12" saucer. There is a mound of Styrofoam peanuts in the middle and the mix is Chilean Sphagnum Moss.

Two views of the plant at its current state (mid-2009). I hope its blooming this fall will be impressive. It is at the peak of its potential for display. The blooms are long and the bulbs in the center that flower won't show them off as well as the ones at the outer edge. By the next blooming, the bulbs in the center will have increased by about 3 times as many and the bulbs at the edge will be grown down, which doesn't display the flowers as nicely.

I have found that plants in the Sestochilus section (*lobbii, clapton-ense, facetum,* etc.) and hybrids with them close their flowers up at night for the first few days. If I try to make crosses before the flowers stay open at night, most times I fail. When I started paying more attention to this timing, I was more successful. I HAVE gotten crosses to take on the first day so it is possible.

Not every flower should be used as a parent. The black object at the bottom is a pencil point.
(*B. moniliforme* C.S.P.Parish & Rchb.f.)
Assam to Indo-China

<u>Chapter 10</u>
***Bulb. ornatissimum* or what?**

This plant has been a problem since before I started growing orchids in 1969.

I spent about 30 hours down at Selby Botanical Gardens going through their files, Pickled specimens in the Herbarium, their Microfiche and Library. Thanks to Wes Higgins and Stig Dalstrom for letting me get underfoot for many weeks and assisting me with endless questions.

Here is what I have been able to determine (and I'm not a taxonomist, I don't even play one on TV).

Bulb. ornatissimum (Rchb.f.) J.J.Sm.

Originally it was called *Cirrhopetalum ornatissimum*. It was described (in 1882) by a German, the son of Heinrich Gottlieb Ludwig Reichenbach, Heinrich Gustav Reichenbach, (hence, the abbreviation, Rchb.f.). Then it was put into the genus *Phyllorchis* by Kuntze in 1891. I know, who cares, but I'm trying to give you the whole story.

Finally the name was changed to *Bulbophyllum ornatissimum* in 1912 by the Dutch botanist Johannes Jacobus Smith (J.J.Sm.).

Now remember, there wasn't email or overnight delivery in those days so lots of plants received many names by many students.

At first, I thought there were only two species in the plants in this group; *B. appendiculatum* Rolfe, described in 1901 [or *B. putidum* (Teijsm. & Binn.) J.J.Sm., described in 1862, as we will see later]; and *B. fascinator* (Rolfe) Rolfe, described in 1908. Now, I am going to amend that thought with this thought, "only a very small number of complete nutsos care about what is named what. However, we WOULD like to know, so here goes."

I still feel that there are only two in this group, but the lumping and splitting are for different reasons. The previous group has only one flower (on rare occasions, robust plants can produce two). There is another grouping of plants that has an umbel of 3-8 flowers, and they have been the source of much of the confusion. Or the catalyst.

B. rothschildianum (O'Brien) J.J.Sm., *B. wendlandianum* (Kraenzl.) J.J.Sm. and *B. ornatissimum* (Rchb.f.) J.J.Sm. are the culprits.

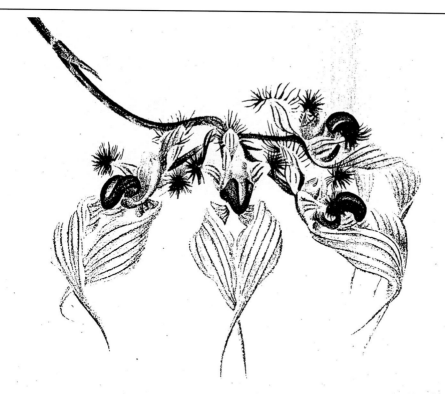

CIRRHOPETALUM ORNATISSIMUM, Rchb.f.

Chromolith J.GOFFIN 1

This is the original line drawing of *B. ornatissimum* in <u>The Gardener's Chronicle</u> of 1882. Note three things; one -- the number of flowers; two -- the short lateral sepals; and three -- the tufts on the ends of the petals which are very different from other species as we will see later.

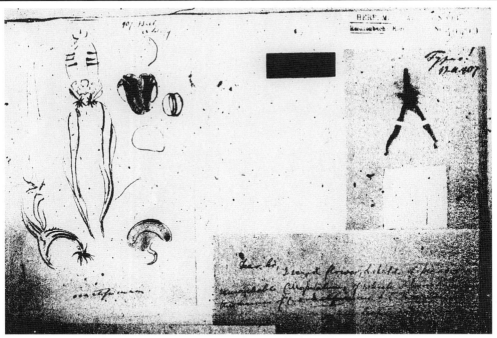

This is the original herbarium sheet (above) and comments (below) in
__The Gardener's Chronicle__ (1882) from Reichenbach. Note the tufts on
the petal in the lower left.

Gard, chron. n.s 18. 4/24 (1882)   Ung. usn-

CIRRHOPETALUM ORNATISSIMUM, *n. sp.*

I have known this fine thing since October, 1879,
when it was sent me by Mr. W. Bull (No. 407). I
received a single flower only. Then it came from Sir
C. W. Strickland and Mr. James O'Brien. Finally I
now find it amidst the flowers arrived during my
absence, both from Messrs. Veitch and Mr. W. Bull.
The flowers are equal to those of Cirrhopetalum
Thouarsii. Their best feature lies in the tremulous
amellæ, which are borrowed from Bulbophyllum
saltatorium. They are sessile around the oblong
triangular cucullate odd sepal and in highest beauty
at the top of the small falcate petals; all of the
darkest brown-purple colour. The flowers are straw
coloured with purple longitudinal lines. Column and
lip light purple. It may come from East India, though
I am not sure of it. It is comparable to Dr. Wight's
C. grandiflorum. *H. G. Rchb. f.*

This is the drawing from Sir Joseph Dalton Hooker in
<u>Curtis's Botanical Magazine</u>; vol. 118, 1892; note the number of flowers,
the size, and the tufts on the petals.

Here are the description and comments by Sir Joseph Dalton Hooker in the <u>Curtis's Botanical Magazine</u>, 1892

Tab. 7229.

CIRRHOPETALUM ORNATISSIMUM.

Native of Assam and the Eastern Himalaya.

Nat. Ord. ORCHIDEÆ.   Tribe EPIDENDREÆ.

Genus CIRRHOPETALUM, *Lindl.* ; (*Benth. & Hook. f. Gen. Plant.*, vol. iii. p. 504.)

CIRRHOPETALUM *ornatissimum;* rhizomate robusto, pseudobulbis ovoideis tetragonis, folio elliptico-lanceolato, scapo suberecto paucifloro, bracteis subulato-lanceolatis, floribus magnis pallide carneis rubro-striatis, sepalo dorsali ovato-lanceolato basi truncato pilis rubris longe ciliato, lateralibus dorsali duplo longioribus attenuato-acuminatis, petalis ovatis fasciculo palearum sanguinearum terminatis, labello breviter stipitato oblongo obtuso incrassato recurvo, columna longiuscula apicem versus utrinque arista porrecta decurva instructa.

C. ornatissimum, *Reichb. f. in Gard. Chron.* 1882, vol. ii. p. 424; *Warner Orchid. Album*, t. 369 ; *Hook. f. Fl. Brit. Ind.* vol. v. p. 773.

The general resemblance of this remarkable plant to the still more remarkable *C. Collettii* figured in this work in October of last year (Plate 7198), is obvious, notwithstanding the marked difference in their pseudobulbs and mode of growth ; the pseudobulbs in this organ being in *ornatissimum* ovate and four-sided, in *Collettii* subglobose and deeply four lobed ; and the scape in this being erect and arising from the side of the pseudobulb as usual in the genus, but in *Collettii* it is pendulous and arises from the young growths before the new pseudobulbs are developed.   Other differences are to be found in the longer leaves of *C. ornatissimum*, the truncate base of the dorsal sepal, which is not tipped with a bunch of paleæ; in the shorter lateral sepals, and especially in the much less highly developed paleæ of the petals, in the scabrid ridges of the lip, and in the bristle-like appendages at the tip of the column not being strongly decurved.

C. ornatissimum was first described from specimens stated to have been received from Assam, the reputed native country of the specimen here figured ; but as, according to a figure in the collection of drawings belonging to the Botanical Gardens of Calcutta, it is a native of

APRIL 1ST, 1892.

Sikkim, its more exact locality is probably the outer ranges of the Himalaya Mountains, from Sikkim eastwards. In the above-mentioned figure the sepals and petals are yellowish-green, and the red streaks are broken up into purple dots. In the plate given in Warner's Orchid Album the leaves are broadly elliptic with rounded retuse tips, dark green with no yellow margin, the bracts are longer and the flowers much larger, of a dull purplish blue, the lateral sepals end in longer tails, and the petals have an almost black purple centre and greenish border ; it doubtless represents a variety.

C. *ornatissimum* was received at Kew from the Royal Botanical Gardens of Calcutta in 1890 (under the erroneous name of *Bulbophyllum Mannii*), and flowered in the tropical orchid house of Kew, in September, 1891.—*J. D. H.*

Fig. 1, Dorsal sepal; 2, paleæ of the petals; 3, column and lip; 4, lip; 5, anther :— *all enlarged.*

28

2. *Bulbophyllum ornatissimum* (REICHENB. f.) J. J. SMITH, Bull. Buitz. 2. s.
8: 26, 1912.

Cirrhopetalum ornatissimum REICHENBACH f., Gard. Chron. 1882, 2: 424; HOOKER
f. 1890: 773 (p.p.); idem in Bot. Mag. T. 7229, 1897; HAINES 1924: 1177.
Phyllorchis ornatissimum (REICHENBACH f.) KUNTZE, Rev. Gen. 2: 677, 1891.

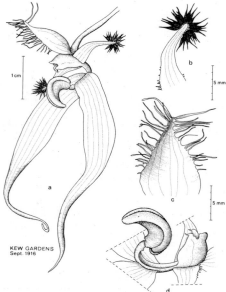

Fig. 2. *Bulbophyllum ornatissimum* (RCHB. f.) J. J. SM. a. flower, b. petal, c. dorsal
sepal, d. lip and column.

Occurrence: Presumably Assam (BULL 407 Herb. REICHENBACH! type, K!; GRIFFITH
fide HOOKER f.); Jashpur (CARDON sine No. fide HAINES).

The type sheet (49499) in Herb. REICHENB. has a single flower marked
type; another flower, presumably from the same plant is in Kew. Also,
in Herb. REICHENB. there is a coloured sketch but apart from these I
have only seen material grown in different nurseries; a sketch of a flower
from a plant grown in Kew in 1916 is given in Fig. 2. As shown by ROLFE
(1901: 148) the plant called *C. ornatissimum* by KING & PANTLING is not
that species, see under *B. putidum* p. 30.

**Here is the line drawing by Seidenfaden in <u>Dansk Botanical Arkiv</u> 1973. Note
the length of the lateral sepals (approx. 5cm or 2 inches) and the tufts on the
petals. Also, note the last sentence in the comments.**

The only awards to *B. ornatissimum* are 'Lil' (AM in 1973 to Lil Severin) and 'Fiddlehead Farm' (CCM in 1985 to Bill & Connie Timm).

AOS Award photo; no photographer listed
'Lil' AM/AOS

<u>THIS IS NOT</u> *B. ornatissimum*!

As you will see, the *B. ornatissimum* 'Lil' is a *B. rothschildianum* and I believe it is the 'Haverhill' clone, also having lateral sepals 12.1 cm long (5 inches).

The 'Fiddlehead Farm' clone is a single flowered plant, having 30 flowers and 12 buds on 42 inflorescences. This plant was large enough to produce umbels if it was in the genes. There is no photograph (Bill Timm per. comm. and Pam Giust, AOS).

Here is the one flower I have found that seems to prove that *B. ornatissimum* actually existed in cultivation at one time. It may still, although I have never seen it, nor have I ever personally known someone to have it. This is the pickled specimen of a flower at Selby Gardens belonging to the late FL Stevenson identified as *B. ornatissimum* (#6678). I looked at 40 different specimens with various names and this is the only one that fits the criteria. I had to photograph it under liquid so the tufts would expand and show up so I'm sorry for the imperfections. It does show all the characteristics perfectly, though. It even shows the lines in the sepals and petals. The last photo is out of the liquid so you can see the lip better and the lines on the sepals and petals.

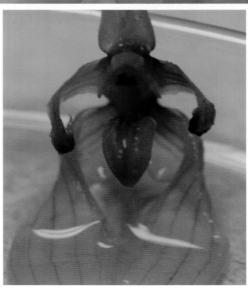

B. rothschildianum and B. wendlandianum are a little easier to separate. First the B. rothschildianum.

Here is the original drawing from <u>The Gardener's Chronicle</u> in 1895. Note the length of the lateral sepals and the hairs all along the petals which lack the tufts on the ends. The color is different as well, but color doesn't count in describing a species (it can count for describing a variety).

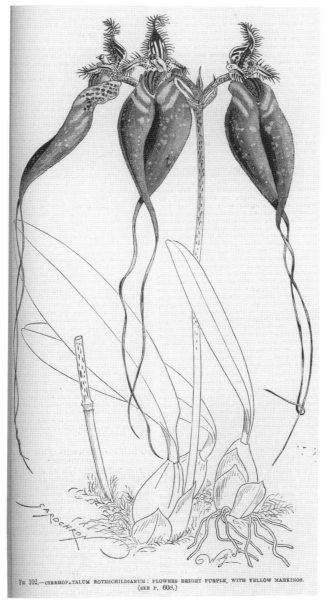

FIG 102.—CIRRHOPETALUM ROTHSCHILDIANUM : FLOWERS BRIGHT PURPLE, WITH YELLOW MARKINGS.
(SEE P. 608.)

Here is a drawing from <u>The Orchids of Sikkim and North East Himalaya</u> by S. Z. Lucksom. The text says that although the plant was purported to come from the Darjeeling area of India, it was never found again. It was rediscovered in 1991 in the Mokokchung District of Nagaland which is between the northwest corner of Myanmar (Burma) and Assam. Note the shape and positioning of the hairs on the dorsal sepal and petals.

Fig. 408 *Mastigion rothschildianum* (O'Brien) S.Z.Lucksom, comb.nov. 1 habitat, 2 front view of a single flower, 3 side view of same with floral bract and pedicellate-ovary, 4 front view of the dorsal sepal, 5 petals, 6 front view of lip, 7 dide view of lip, 8 side view of pedicellate-ovary column, its foot and lip, 9 close view of tip of column, 10 side view of tip of ovary, column with anther in situ, its foot, 11 view of column devoid of anther, 12 various view of anther, 13 pollinia.

Here is a photograph from an F3 generation seedling

It is my guess that the first few *B. rothschildianum* plants were tetraploids (which have a double set of chromosomes. This occurs when the chromosomes divide prior to the cell splitting, and then the cell doesn't split for some reason. Now the cell has a double set. This can occur either in nature or be induced in the lab). In growing several generations of seedlings, I believe I used parents that were both tetraploids, resulting in tetraploid seedlings. This has been beneficial because now we have lots of different plants that are all (or most) tetraploids.

The original plant was found in a box of "nearly dead orchid plants" by James O'Brien at Mr. Stevens' in 1892, said to be from "the hills above Darjeeling." The plants were sent to Lord Rothschild and subsequently flowered in 1895, at which time they were named by James O'Brien for Rothschild.[12]

---

12   Thanks to Ken Roberts who has more books than most libraries, actually reads them and is kind enough to share his knowledge with me. This info came from <u>The Orchid Review</u>, December, 1922

Now the *B. wendlandianum*. Friedrich Wilhelm Ludwig Kraenzlin described a plant he saw in May of 1891 which beat out Joseph Dalton Hooker's description of a plant Hooker described in October of 1891 (*B. collettii*), so *B. wendlandianum* is correct and not *B. collettii*. Here is the description and drawing by Kraenzlin.

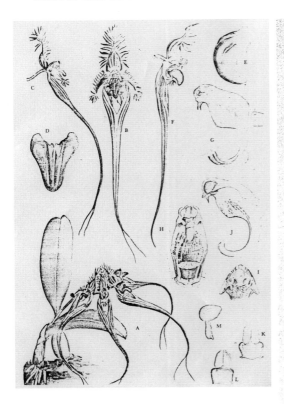

NEW OR NOTEWORTHY PLANTS.

CIRRHOPETALUM WENDLANDIANUM, *n. sp.*

IMAGINE a Cirrhopetalum, which is a combination of C. Medusæ and C. fimbriatum, the enormous tails of the former being attached in this case to the petals, which has given the general appearance, of the sepals, but not the fluttering leaflets of the top, and then this flower, coloured in the way of old C. auratum, and you will have an idea of a very striking plant. To give a correct description, we must add the following characters :—The bulbs are small, three-quarters of an inch high, about half-an-inch broad, and a quarter-of-an-inch thick, crowned by a single lanceolate leaf. The flower-stalk rises from three or four brownish-green sheets, grows to a height of 3 or 4 inches, and bears a little umbel of three to six flowers. The sepals are ovate, concave pointed, and with long hairs on the whole margin, as is observable in many other species of Bulbophyllum and Cirrhopetalum. From the top or point of the sepals rise five or six fluttering, very tender, serrulate leaflets of about the same length as the sepals, of a deep claret-red colour. The petals are ovate at the base, protracted into tails from 6 to 7 inches in length, longer than the pedicel itself. The labellum is very small, triangular, blunt at the top, and bent downwards. The column is short-winged above, and also bent downwards to the lip ; the colour of both is purplish, with deep red spots or little blotches.

This curious plant flowered for the first time in the March of this year at Mr. Wendland's, Herren-hausen, near Hanover, but it was bought in England, being imported from British Burmah. We received from Mr. Wendland a splendid flower-stalk, and a very characteristic drawing of the whole plant, which is to be published in Part V. of the *Xenia Orchidacea*. [See C. Colletti, p. 614. ED.] *Dr. F. Kränzlin, Berlin.*

This is the description and drawing by Hooker of *B. collettii* from <u>Curtis's Botanical Magazine</u>, 1891. Note the shape of the tufts on the petals and the spike emerging from the new growth.

Tᴀʙ. 7198.

CIRRHOPETALUM Cᴏʟʟᴇᴛᴛɪɪ.

Native of the Shan States.

Nat. Ord. Oʀᴄʜɪᴅᴇᴀ.—Tribe Eᴘɪᴅᴇɴᴅʀᴇᴀ.

Genus Cɪʀʀʜᴏᴘᴇᴛᴀʟᴜᴍ, *Lindl.; (Benth. et Hook. f. Gen. Pl.* vol. iii. p. 504.)

Cɪʀʀʜᴏᴘᴇᴛᴀʟᴜᴍ *Collettii;* rhizomate robusto, pseudobulbis 4-lobis, folio elliptico- v. oblongo-lanceolato, scapo robusto deflexo 5–6 flore, bracteis subulato-lanceolatis, floribus magnis aurantiacis rubro striatis, sepalo dorsali triangulari-ovato caudato, cauda, marginibusque paleis membranaceis elongatis mobilibus creberrime onustis, sepalis lateralibus dorsali pluries longioribus in caudas gracillimas sensim angustatis, petalis ovato-rotundatis acuminatis apicibus fasciculo palearum instructis, labello breviter stipitato oblongo obtuso incrassato recurvo, columna longiuscula apicem versus utrinque arista decurva instructa.

C. Collettii, *Hemsl. in Hook. f. Fl. Brit. Ind.* vol. vi. p. 773; *in Journ. Linn. Soc.* vol. xxviii. p. 131, t. 20 (errore *Collettianum*).

Cirrhopetalum Collettii is certainly in many respects the most singular species of the genus hitherto discovered, though in so far as its peculiarities of structure are concerned, these differ only in degree of development from what obtain in species already known. Thus, as Mr. Hemsley well observes, *C. Collettii* is nearest in affinity to *C. ornatissimum* of the Eastern Himalaya, in which the petals are tipped with a bunch of slender mobile red paleæ. It is also nearly allied to *C. fimbriatum* of Bombay, figured at tab. 4391 of this work, the dorsal sepals and petals of which are margined with long slender paleæ attached, as in the plant here figured, by so minute a point as to be in constant motion. In neither of these, however, are the paleæ dilated, cuneiform and lacerate, as are the terminal and often the lateral ones of the dorsal sepal of *C. Collettii*, and in those of the bundle that tips the petals.

Mr. Hemsley has pointed out to me a peculiarity in the mode of growth of this species, in that the flowering scape is not formed at the base of a fully formed pseudobulb, but is developed together with a young leaf which afterwards forms a pseudobulb, and is enclosed in sheaths with it, as shown in the drawing. I observe the same

Oᴄᴛᴏʙᴇʀ 1ꜱᴛ, 1891.

phenomena in *Bulbophyllum fusco-purpureum*, but not in any other species of *Bulbophyllum* or *Cirrhopetalum* that I have examined, though it no doubt may occur in others.

The flowering of this beautiful plant enables me to correct two errors that have crept into the descriptions which were made from dried specimens. One of these (in the Flora of British India) describes the pseudobulbs as very small; the other (in the Linnean Journal) figures and describes the peduncle as erect.

C. Collettii was discovered by Major-General Collett, C.B., F.L.S., in the Southern Shan hills, when on service there during the late Burmese war, and is one of a fine collection of plants, amounting to upwards of seven hundred species, of which twelve per cent. were new, made chiefly by this distinguished officer in that previously unvisited and indeed inaccessible region. These are enumerated, with descriptions of the new species, by Mr. Hemsley in the Journal of the Linnean Society cited above; and the enumeration is prefaced by a valuable essay (accompanied by a good map) on the climate and vegetation of the ¦Shan hills, by General Collett himself. Amongst other plants the *Cirrhopetalum* is noted as highly curious, and meriting notice; the flower, which is inodorous, being "remarkable for the extremely long attenuated sepals, which are highly mobile and are wafted about by the slightest breath of air; and for the flower being also furnished with a number of little streamers or banner-like appendages, which, as Darwin remarks of an allied *Bulbophyllum* (*B. lemniscatum*, Plate 5961), when blown by a breath of wind wriggle about in a very odd manner."

Another plant discovered by General Collett is *R. gigantea*, Collett (Hemsley, l.c. 55, t. 9), a white-flowered species allied to *R. indica*, with flowers five inches in diameter, and which is flourishing at Kew, though it has not as yet flowered.

Live plants of *Cirrhopetalum Collettii* were sent to the Royal Gardens by its discoverer in 1888, where the plant here figured flowered in May of the present year.— *J. D. H.*

Fig. 1, Dorsal sepal; 2, petal; 3, palea from the latter; 4, column and lip; 5, column; 6, anther; 7, pollinia :—*all enlarged.*

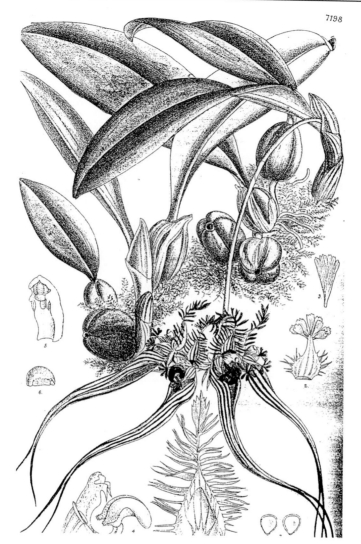

Aside from differences in the plants, the flowers and the blooming style, *B. rothschildianum* and *B. wendlandianum* are identical. Just kidding. Those are major differences and make them different species. The easiest way to tell them apart is when and how they bloom. *B. wendlandianum* has thin flowers and blooms out of an unformed new growth in the spring (as is shown in the drawings) and *B. rothschildianum* has very wide flowers (mostly) and blooms out of a mature growth in the fall. *B. wendlandianum* also has micro-tufts on the petals where *B. rothschildianum* does not.

B. wendlandianum   **B. rothschildianum**

Here is the drawing of *Bulb. wendlandianum* from Seidenfaden in <u>Orchid Genera in Thailand V111</u>; pg 151. Note the different shape of the tufts on petals from *B. rothschildianum* and the spike emerging from the new growth.

.080m (GT 5014 C!); Ban Klong Noi 900m (Cumb. 1175 C!); Bo Luang (GT 3281, 5201, 5204, 5252 C!); Doi Chang Sa, Mae Chem 200m (Kerr 417 BK! C! K!); Pha Kampheng, Chomtong 1500m (Suvarn 335 BKF!); North of Mon

Khet (GT 8336 C!); Northeast of Khun Mae Surin (GT 8439 C!).
Distribution: Northern Burma.

See Fig. 100.

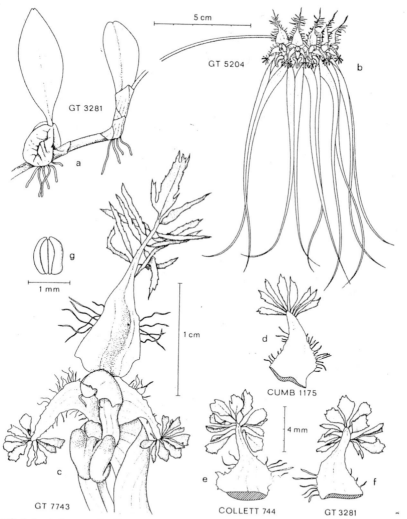

Fig. 100. *Bulbophyllum wendlandianum* (Krzl.) Dammer. a. plant, b. inflorescence, c. flower except lateral sepals, d.–f. petals, g. pollinia. e. from the type specimen of *Cirrhopetalum collettii* Hemsl.

Now on to the tricky ones, *B. putidum* (Teijsm. & Binn.) J.J.Sm.,
B. appendiculatum (Rolfe) J.J.Sm. and *B. fascinator* (Rolfe) Rolfe.
Let's start with *B. fascinator* since it is more distinct.

Here is the original drawing and description by Robert Allen Rolfe in
<u>Curtis's Botanical Magazine</u> in 1908. Note the bumps on the lateral sepals;
the amount and position of the "feathers" on the dorsal sepal and petals;
and the smooth furrow in the center of the lip.

BULBOPHYLLUM FASCINATOR.

Annam.

ORCHIDACEAE. Tribe EPIDENDREAE.
BULBOPHYLLUM, *Thouars; Benth. et Hook. f. Gen. Plant.* vol. iii. p. 501.

Bulbophyllum fascinator, Rolfe; a *B. appendiculato*, Rolfe, floribus multo majoribus, segmentorum appendicibus linearibus non foliaceis differt.

Herba epiphytica. *Rhizoma* repens, validum. *Pseudobulbi* ovoideo-oblongi, obscure tetragoni, nitidi, 1·5–2·5 cm. longi, monophylli. *Folia* sessilia, coriacea, elliptico-oblonga, obtusa, 5 cm. longa, 1·5–3 cm. lata. *Scapi* patentes, circa 10 cm. longi, uniflori. *Bracteae* spathaceae, apice acuteae, 1 cm. longae. *Flores* magni, pallide virides, purpureo-punctati et ornati. *Sepalum posticum* ovatum, acuminatum, 2·5–3 cm. longum, supra medium ciliatum et appendicibus filiformibus amethystino-purpureis ornatum; sepala lateralia connata, oblongo-lanceolata, longissime caudato-acuminata, 13–18 cm. longa, basi coriacea, crebre verrucosa, marginibus revolutis. *Petala* falcato-oblonga, subacuta, circa 2 cm. longa, margine et apice appendicibus filiformibus amethystino-purpureis ornata. *Labellum* recurvum, ovato-oblongum, subobtusum, canaliculatum, bicarinatum, carinis et marginibus puberulis. *Columna* lata, 8 mm. longa, marginibus acutis, dentibus subulatis, basi obscure tridenticulatis.—*Cirrhopetalum fascinator*, Rolfe in Kew Bulletin, 1908, p. 69.

The remarkable species here figured is a native of Annam, where it was discovered by Mr. W. Micholitz, when collecting for Messrs. Sander & Sons. Living plants were sent home, one of which flowered at Kew in September, 1907, when the species was described under the name of *Cirrhopetalum fascinator*, Rolfe. The genus *Cirrhopetalum*, however, merges so imperceptibly into *Bulbophyllum* that the two are now regarded as indistinguishable, hence the adoption here of the older generic name. *Bulbophyllum fascinator* is nearly allied to the Himalayan *B. appendiculatum*, Rolfe (*Cirrhopetalum ornatissimum*, King & Pantl. in Ann. R. Bot. Gard. Calc. vol. viii. p. 95, t. 133, not of Reichb. f.), but has much larger flowers, with various structural differences. It is a member of a small group characterised by its solitary-flowered scapes, containing the following additional species :—*Bulbophyllum merguense*, Par. & Reichb. f., *B. lasioglossum*, Par. & Reichb. f., *B. antenniferum*,

JUNE, 1908.

Reichb. f., *B. maxillare*, Reichb. f., *B. breviscapum*, Ridl.
(*Cirrhopetalum breviscapum*, Rolfe, Bot. Mag. t. 8033), and
two or three imperfectly known Malayan species. All of
these were formerly considered to be anomalous species of
Cirrhopetalum, having the floral structure though not the
remarkable umbellate inflorescence of the genus. The
elongation of, and frequently the union of the lateral
sepals constituted the most marked character of *Cirrhopetalum*, and it is unfortunate that the occurrence of
species of intermediate character should render it un-
tenable.

DESCRIPTION.—*Epiphyte* with stout creeping rhizome.
Pseudobulbs approximate, ovoid-oblong, obscurely tetra-
gonous, shining, $\frac{3}{4}$–1 in. long, 1-leaved. *Leaves* sessile,
elliptical-oblong, obtuse, coriaceous, about 2 in. long, over
1 in. broad. *Scape* suberect, about 4 in. long, 1-flowered.
Bracts spathaceous, acute, $\frac{1}{3}$ in. long. *Flowers* large, pale
green with crimson markings. *Dorsal sepal* ovate, acumi-
nate, about $1\frac{1}{4}$ in. long, with crimson filiform appendages
above the apex, ciliate towards the base; lateral sepals
united, oblong-lanceolate below, then prolonged into long
caudate appendages, about 7 in. long, the basal part
coriaceous, verrucose, with revolute margin. *Petals* falcate-
oblong, subacute, under $\frac{1}{2}$ in. long, the margin and apex
bearing numerous crimson filiform appendages. *Lip*
recurved, ovate-oblong, subobtuse, channelled, bicarinate,
with the keels and margins puberulous. *Column* broad,
$\frac{1}{3}$ in. long, with acute margins and acute slightly tridenticu-
late teeth.—R. A. ROLFE.

Here is a close-up picture of a live specimen showing the identifying details of *B. fascinator*. Note the exact match with the original drawing in all details.

Now let's look at *Bulb. appendiculatum* Rolfe
Here is the original description and drawing by Rolfe from the
<u>Kew Bulletin</u> in 1901

Kew Bulletin (1901): 148.

246. **Cirrhopetalum appendiculatum,** *Rolfe;* inter. affines ad *C. merguensem,* Par. et Reichb. f., accedit; differt sepalis lateralibus longe attenuatis.

Rhizoma repens. *Pseudobulbi* subdistantes, oblongi, subcostati, 1 poll. longi, 5 lin. lati, monophylli. *Folia* elliptica, emarginata, coriacea, sessilia, 2 poll. longa, 11 lin. lata. *Scapi* erecti, 3 poll. alti, quisque medio vagina lanceolata carinata obtectus uniflorus; bractea lanceolata, acuminata, carinata, 5 lin. longa. *Sepalum* posticum ovatum, concavum, apice caudato-setiferum, 8 lin. longum, prope apicem appendicibus foliaceis instructum; lateralia basi libera, dein fere ad apicem connata, longe attenuato-caudata marginibus involutis, apice bifida, filiformia, 2¾–3 poll. longa. *Petala* falcato-incurva, lineari-oblonga, acuminata, 4 lin. longa, prope apicem appendicibus foliaceis instructa. *Labellum* magnum, carnosum, recurvum, ovato-oblongum, obtusum, glabrum, 4½ lin. longum, basi concavum, marginibus erectis, disco tricarinato. *Columna* crassa, 2 lin. longa, dentibus brevibus obtusis.—*C. ornatissimum,* Hook. f. Fl. Brit. Ind. v., 773, ex parte (non Reichb. f.); King & Pantl. in Ann. Roy. Bot. Gard. Calc. viii. 95, t. 133.

INDIA: Sikkim, in warm valleys, *Pantling,* 197.

Flowered in the collection of H. J. Elwes, Esq., Colesbourne, Gloucestershire, in October, 1896. The dorsal sepal and petals are pale yellow, of these the dorsal sepal has three dull purple veins and a few spots near the margin, the petals have a single vein, and all are terminated by numerous purple leaf-like appendages attached by a filiform base. The lateral sepals are speckled with reddish purple on a lighter ground. The lip is rosy purple with dark purple margins, keels and numerous spots. It is very distinct from *C. ornatissimum,* Reichb. f., with which it has been confused.

Note the last sentence at the end of the description.

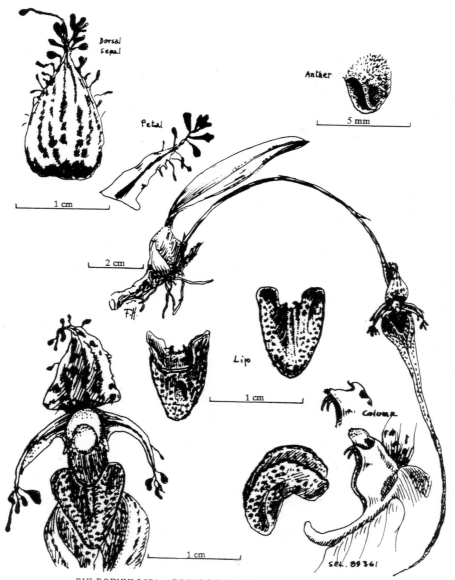

BULBOPHYLLUM APPENDICULATUM (Rolfe)J.J.Sm.

**Note the shape of the flower;
the form and placement of the "feathers" on the
dorsal sepal and petals;
the ridges in the center of the lip ;
and the lack of bumps on the lateral
sepals, (the dots are color, not form).**

Here is a drawing from <u>The Orchids of Sikkim and N. E. Himalaya</u> by S. Z. Lucksom with a close-up of the lip. The plants in the genus *Mastigion* have been changed back to *Bulbophyllum*.

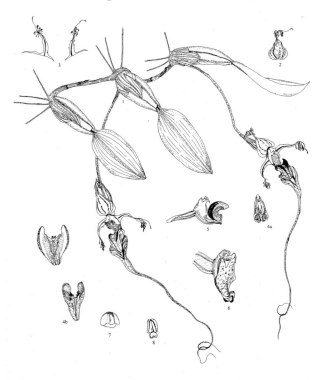

Fig. 407 *Mastigion appendiculatum* (Rolfe) Garay, Hamer and Seigreist in Nord. J.Bot.14: 637 (1994). Fig 1 habitat, 2 dorsal sepal, 3 petals, 4 (a) natural view of lip, 4(b) dorsal and front view of lip, 5 lateral view of pedicellate ovary, column, foot and lip, 6 a part of ovary and front view of column showing, stigma and foot, 7 anther, 8 pollinia.

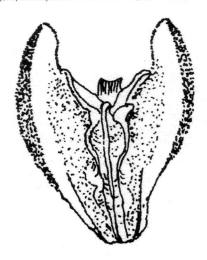

Here is the original description of *Cirr. putidum* in <u>Natuurkundig Tijdschrift Voor Nederlandsch-Indie Jakarta</u> vol. 24; pg 311, **published in 1862** by Johannes Elias Teijsmann and Simon Binnendijk (Teijsm & Binn) it was changed to *Bulbophyllum putidum* in 1912 by J.J. Smith

PLANTAE

NOVAE IN

HORTO BOGORIENSI CULTAE,

AUCTORIBUS

J. E. TEIJSMANN ET S. BINNENDIJK.

14. CIRRHOPETALUM *putidum* nob.

C. rhizomate repente, pseudobulbis 4- angularibus, ovatis, sulcatis; foliis oblongis obtusis emarginatis; scapis filiformibus unifloris, bracteis ovario duplo minoribus, perigonii phyllis ciliatis, exterioribus lateralibus longissimis, apicibus spiraliter involutis, dorsali ovato, oblongo, acuminato, subcucullato, acumine reflexo, interioribus dorsali duplo minoribus, linearibus, labello ovato-oblongo, acuto, profunde caniculato, 3 lineis elevatis notato; gynostemii cornibus obtusis, apiculatis, marginibus alatis, stigmate cuneato.

Habit. *Palembang*, TEIJSMANN.

Pseudobulbus 0,03 longus, 0,024 latus. Folia 0,1 longa, 0,024 lata, supra lucida. Phylla perigonialia exteriora 0,12 longa, viridi-lutescentia, violaceo-maculata, dorsale 0,015 longum, apice 0,007 longum, interiora 0,009 longa, 0,002 lata, ciliis ad basin incrassatam albis, apicem versus violaceis. Odor Ari maculati.

Here is the translation graciously provided by Dr. Eleni Manolaraki, Assistant Professor of Classics at the University of South Florida in Tampa:

Rhizome from the side, pseudobulb 4-angled, ovoid, furrowed; leaves oblong with smooth margins; flower spike fuzzy, one flowered; petals smaller than dorsal sepal, ciliate, with linear stripes marked with raised lines; lateral sepals long, inwardly twisted; dorsal sepal ovate, oblong, pointed and cupped with tip pointed backward; lip oval and oblong, pointed with deep canals, marked with 3 elevated lines; column with flat horns, pointed tip and winged margins, stigma wedge-shaped; pseudobulb .03 long x .024 wide; leaves shiny on top; sepals reverse yellow-green, spotted violet; dorsal sepal with small tip; fringe with white base and solid violet top; smell of spotted arum.

As you can see, this description matches quite well with the *B. appendiculatum*. Since it predates the *B. appendiculatum* by almost 40 years, it is the proper name to use.

115

Here is a bit of a problem that cropped up in my research. In speaking with Ken Roberts, he mentioned that it might be possible to get a drawing of *B. putidum* from the Herbarium at Leiden, in the Netherlands. He contacted Ed de Vogel who very kindly responded quickly and this is what we recieved:

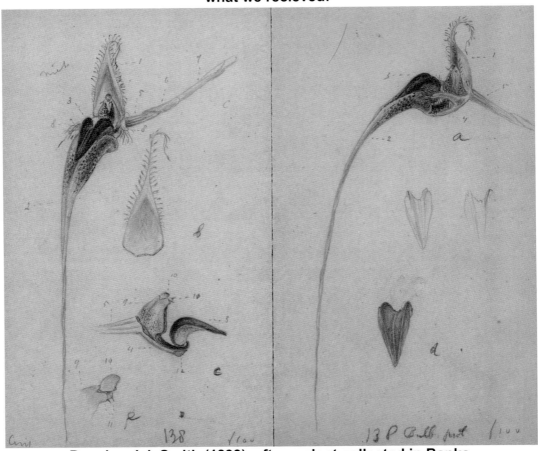

Drawing J.J. Smith (1899), after a plant collected in Banka,
©Nationaal Herbarium Nederland, Leiden branch.

As you can see, the problem is that this is a drawing of *B. fascinator*. Smith changed the name from *Cirrhopetalum* to *Bulbophyllum* in 1912 and could have confused or forgotten his drawing, the original description, the subsequent publication of *B. appendiculatum* or any number of other identifications of the various species in this section. In any event, my feelings about *B. putidum* being the correct name still stand.

Here is Seidenfaden's drawing of, and comments (next page) on, *B. putidum.*
Please note in the comments that the drawing is from a flower in the Leiden
Herbarium presumably from Bankra and is probably Smith's model as well.

5. *Bulbophyllum putidum* (TEIJSM. & BINNEND.) J. J. SMITH, Bull. Buitz.
2. s. 8: 27, 1912.

J. J. SMITH 1930: T. 97, III; idem 1933: 324; SEIDENFADEN 1972: 111, Fig. 29.

Cirrhopetalum putidum TEIJSMANN & BINNENDIJK, Nat. Tijds. Ned. Ind. 23: 311,
1862.

Cirrhopetalum ornatissimum auct., non REICHENBACH f.; KING & PANTLING 1898:
95, T. 122; PRAIN 1903: 759; AMES & QUISUMBING 1931: 380, Pl. 16; HARA 1966:
427.

Cirrhopetalum appendiculatum ROLFE, Kew Bull. 1901: 148, syn. nov; HOOKER f.,
1890: 773 (p.p.).

Bulbophyllum appendiculatum (ROLFE) J. J. SMITH, Bull. Buitz. 2. s. 8: 22, 1912,
syn. nov; Gard. Chron. 3. s. 57: 38, Fig., 1915.
Occurrence: Sikkim (PANTLING 197, type of *C. appendiculatum* K!L!M!P!W!, also
fide HARA).
Bengal: Chota Nagpur (fide PRAIN sub nom. *C. ornatissimum*).
?Peninsular Thailand & Malaya: Questionable, see under *B. fascinator.*
Sumatra: Palembang (TEIJSMANN type; JACOBSEN 393 fide J. J. SMITH); Lam-
poeng, Mingalla (GUSDORF 114 K!); sine loc. (cult Bogor W!).
Bangka: fide J. J. SMITH.
Borneo: Kampoeng, Soenkei (fide J. J. SMITH's mss. in L).
Philippines: Mt. Marayap, Zembales, Luzon (RAMOS & EDANO 44806 AMES!).

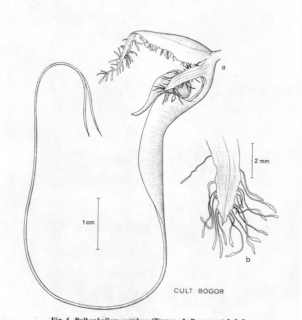

1 cm

2 mm

CULT. BOGOR

Fig. 5. *Bulbophyllum putidum* (TEIJSM. & BINNEND.) J. J. SM.
a. flower, b. tip of petal.

I have not seen TEIJSMANN's type; there are specimens from Sumatra and Bangka in Paris, the specimen located in Leiden from which the flower in Fig. 5 is sketched is presumably from Bangka. In a recent paper (1972: 111) I suggested that ROLFE's *C. appendiculatum* might be the same species, and further studies support this; in one of J. J. SMITH's manu-script notes in Leiden he writes "very related to *B. putidum*", so he seems to have been of the same opinion. Evidently also the records by PRAIN and HARA refer to this species, PRAIN speaks of "usually solitary flower" and mentions that the lateral sepals are 3–4 inches long.

As here understood, *B. putidum* is the most wide spread among its allies, found from the Philippines through Indonesia to Sikkim. In north-ern Indochina we find its very close relative, *B. fascinator*; in the north-western corner from northern Thailand to Nepal we find clearly related species, *B. wendlandianum* and *B. ornatissimum* with its long-flowered form *B. rotschildianum*.

Here is a close-up of the main characteristics of *B. putidum*. The fact that a drawing wasn't published with the original description added to the con-fusion, but with the translation of the *B. putidum*, I am convinced that the name should stand. It also has a pronounced odor which is reflected in the name, and is mentioned in the description.

Now -- here is a drawing from the
Annals of the Royal Botanical Gardens, Calcutta, Vol 8.
I believe this is the major culprit to the problems all these years. As you
can see, this is a *B. putidum* and not a *B. ornatissimum*. It was erroneously
thought to be correct over the years since *B. ornatissimum* wasn't in circulation probably due to extreme rarity.

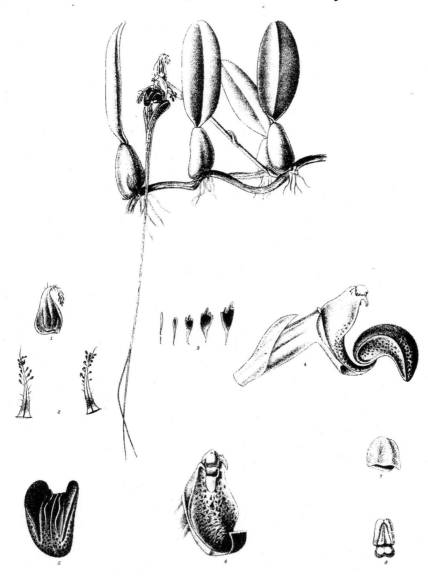

R. Pantling del.

CIRRHOPETALUM ORNATISSIMUM, Reichb. fil.

Lith: by A. C. Singh

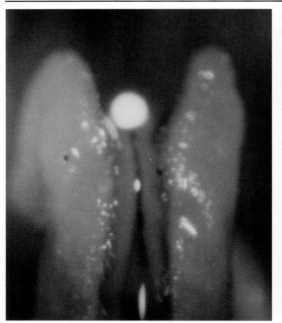
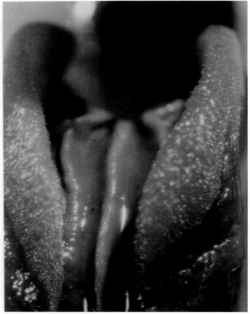

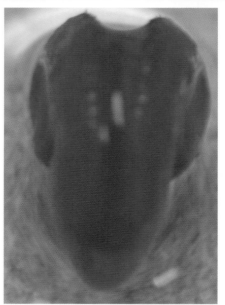

On top are two lips of plants incorrectly listed as *B. ornatissimum* identified many years ago. Note the distinct ridges in the lip. As you can see, they are *B. putidum*. On the bottom is a close-up of the lip of the true *B. ornatissimum* without the ridges.

Now, here are *B. putidum* and *B. fascinator* side by side so you can see the distinct differences between the two.

Finally, the last in this group shouldn't be here at all. It was included in Emly Siegerist's book; <u>The Bulbophyllums and their Allies</u> as one of the species in the genus *Mastigion*. However, I subscribe to the feelings of Gunnar Seidenfaden in this instance.

The plant is called *B. proboscideum* (Gagnep.) Seidenf. & Smitin.

Here are the description and drawing:

<u>Bulbophyllum proboscideum</u> (GAGNEP.) SEIDENF. & SMITIN., Orch. Thail. 1961: 354.

GAGNEPAIN 1931: 6 & 1934: 291 sub nom. *Cirrhopetalum proboscideum.*

Occurrence: II: Nong Khai (THOREL s.n.P! type specimen)

Distribution: Thailand, Laos (Bassac THOREL P!)

In Orchids of Thailand we expressed the feeling that this species could be rather close to *B. lasiochilum.* I have now received THOREL's collections from Paris; unfortunately there are only two quite mutilated flowers, so my sketch in Fig. 26 is rather unsatisfactory. It is, however, obvious that we here have a species which stands quite isolated in the genus, the sepals being placed at the distal end of a long drawn out columnfoot, free at their proximal third, but then united in a long thin tube. Close study of fresh material might show that it should rather be moved to another genus such as *Monomeria.*

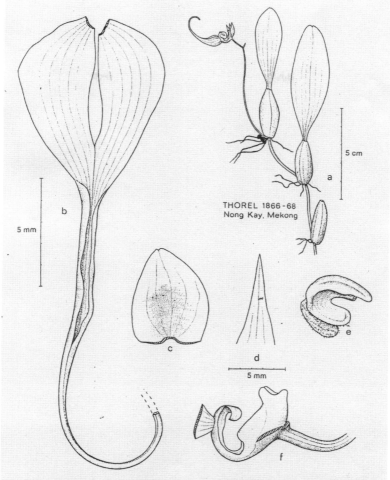

Fig. 26. *Bulbophyllum proboscideum* (GAGNEP.) SEIDENF. & SMITIN. a: plant, b: lateral sepals, tips broken off, c: dorsal sepal, d: petal, e: lip, f: column and column foot.

As you can see, this species has no relation to any of the other species in these sections.

I hope this clears up many of the confusions among the species in this section grown and used in hybridizing. Now we just have to correct the many mistakes already on our tags.

Chapter 11
Bulb. fletcherianum or *Bulb. phalaenopsis* or *Bulb. spiesii...* or what?

B. phalaenopsis J.J.Sm.

B. fletcherianum Rolfe

Here is another area of confusion. It needn't be. There was a pretty good article in the publication, <u>Orchids Australia</u>, April 1999 by Anton Sieder of the Vienna Botanical Gardens, titled Bulbophyllum, Section Macrobulbum.

I say pretty good because he copies a key partly based on data from Yukawa & Kurasawa.

Here is the disputed **(by me)** section of the key:

2. sepals hirsute on the outer side.............*B. phalaenopsis*
2a. sepals not hirsute on the outside..............   =3
3. five to eight flowers per inflorescence,
    lateral sepals 9 to 10cm long...................*B. fletcherianum*
3a. up to 20 flowers per inflorescence,
    lateral sepals up to 7cm long...................*B. spiesii*

So here is the problem. It is not acceptable to separate plants into different species based on the number of flowers such as "5 to 8" or "up to 20." It can be used when describing a plant that only has one flower as opposed to a plant that has many more than one, provided there are other differences, such as flower form. Nor is it acceptable to separate them by very slight differences in the size of a flower part, in this case, the length of sepals. The problem arises when you have plants growing under different conditions. We have all seen that some growers consistently grow more robust plants that flower with larger flowers and more of them. There are also clones that are different as to the size and number of flowers. Observe plants *in situ* growing in the same area and, even there, it is obvious that some plants have flowers that are better than others. Not to mention that you would expect to have slightly smaller flowers if you had 3 times as many.

It should be fairly simple to reach the conclusion that *B. spiesii* Garay, et al. is a nom. illeg. (nomen illegitimum, or illegitimate name) and the correct name for plants without hairs on the outside of the sepals is *B. fletcherianum* Rolfe. At least that is what I will call them until I am shown more definitive reasons to change.

There is no reason to dispute the name *B. phalaenopsis*, which is very different from the previous two.

Chapter 12
Bulb. lobbii as a parent

Bulb. lobbii Lindl. has been used extensively in hybridizing for several reasons. It blooms easily for just about everyone, it is very widespread so there are many forms and the flowers are generally fairly large. Here are some of the best:

B. lobbii 'Kathy's Gold' AM/AOS
Colossus variety from Java

B. lobbii 'A-doribil Too' AM/AOS
Polystictum form from Borneo
Grown from seed

B. lobbii 'A-doribil Peach'
Variety from the Philippines

B. lobbii 'Ashlar' AM/AOS
Plant from Doris Jensen

B. lobbii
From Malacca, Malaysia
Plant from Andy Philips

B. lobbii 'Sorella'
From Palawan Island, Philippines

B. lobbii 'Goldbug'
From lowland Sumatra

B. lobbii 'Bronze Delight' AM/AOS
From mid-level Sumatra

B. veitchianum 'Borneo'   **'A-doribil' CHM-HCC/AOS**

Considered a synonym of B. lobbii by some

©Lewis Ellsworth

B. claptonense 'D&B' CHM/AOS

**From Sabah, Borneo; considered a synonym of B. lobbii by some,
but very different; note the pronounced callus on lip.**

B. claptonense 'A-doribil'

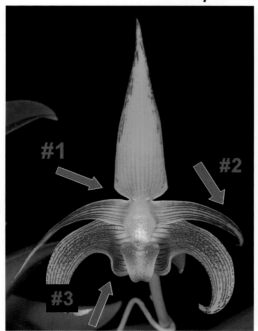

Now, here are some VERY dominant characteristics that are passed to the progeny. The narrowing at the base of the dorsal sepal (#1),
the swept back petals (#2) and
the undulation on the bottom margin of the lateral sepals (#3).
It is very evident in *lobbii* 'Kathy's Gold' and this clone has been used extensively in hybridizing.

Some of the hybrids with *B. lobbii* are:

B. Jersey 'A-doribil' AM/AOS
(*lobbii X echinolabium*)

AOS award photo; no photographer listed
B. Tsiku Taurus 'Megan Garrison' HCC/AOS
(*leysianum X lobbii*)
B. leysianum is an unknown species. The plant used was probably in the
Lepidorhiza Section, perhaps a dark *B. levanae* or one of its synonyms,
B. nymphopolitanum or *B. trigonosepalum*.

B. Frank Smith 'Golden Star'
(*carunculatum X lobbii*)

©Jim Clarkson

B. Jim Clarkson 'Bill Thoms' FCC/AOS
(*lobbii X claptonense*)

B. Jim Krull 'Tuesday'
(*lobbii X ornatissimum**)
*Correctly: *putidum*

B. Stars and Stripes 'A-doribil Too' HCC/AOS
(*lobbii X bicolor* Lindl.)

Bulb. Jim McGoogan
(*sumatranum X veitchianum*)
Some consider both parents synonyms of *B. lobbii*,
so this is considered by some, (not by me), as a *B. lobbii*

B. A-doribil LoNan
(*lobbii* X Nannu Nannu)

134

These characteristics show up even into the 2nd generation (so far) as shown here in the cross of B. A-doribil Super Star 'A-doribil' AM/AOS (Stars and Stripes X *echinolabium*).

Also, these examples are some of the best formed flowers out of the crosses, which is one of the reasons they received awards.

The bulbs of *B. lobbii* are 2 - 6 cm apart and the leaves are fairly wide and soft. These are also passed on to most progeny but they aren't really a characteristic noticed by the judges although it can be important to breeders. The larger internodal length means more space is required for the plants and the softer leaves means greater susceptibility to bugs and pathogens (fungi and bacteria) as well as drooping over the rhizomes, (which is where the flowers arise) and can obstruct them.

Crossing with plants that have stiffer, more upright leaves and closer bulbs, such as plants in the Lepidorhiza Section, can overcome these potential problems. The B. A-doribil Super Star is a good example.

The different forms of *B. lobbii* flower at various times during the year, primarily from early spring to the fall. Making the same cross with different forms can result in the same named hybrid blooming at any time of the year. I am trying to produce this with several hybrids now.

Chapter 13
The Species

There are more than 2500 species in the genus. Here is a SMALL sampling that I feel are easy to grow, fairly easy to obtain and worth the time and effort to grow. Everyone has their own likes and dislikes; these are some of my favorites.

©Don Wilson

B. kermesinum 'A-doribil'

A delightful plant from New Guinea with 4-5" tall flowers. Blooms along the rhizome from June to December. The "asteroids" on the ends of the petals are osmophores, which are scent glands to attract the pollinators. No odor.

©Donald Wilson

Bulb. unitubum J.J.Sm.
This is similar to *kermesinum* in size, country of origin and scent glands. No odor.

Bulb. sigaldiae Guillaumin
Vietnam. Dime-sized flowers in clusters. Plants grow shady, moist and appear very similar to *B. dayanum* Rchb.f. Rambling. No odor.

Bulb. inunctum J.J.Sm.
Peninsular Malaysia, Philippines to Borneo
3-4" flowers produced all along the rhizome close to the plant.
Flowers sporadically throughout the year. No odor.

Bulb. pardalotum Garay, Hamer & Siegerist
Philippines
Small plants with large flowers on wiry stems. Interesting thing is the flowers open in the morning and close by about 10 AM. Open again for several days. Easy to grow and flower. No odor.

Bulb. medusae (Lindl.) Rchb.f. Clone from Max Thompson & Bryon Rinke
Peninsular Thailand to West Malaysia
A very common and famous species. Grows very bright and warm. Give lots of water to the roots when in bud for long heads of flowers. Do not get the flowers wet or they will go brown and drop. Mild odor.

Fairly rare, a heavily-spotted clone of *Bulb. medusae* 'A-doribil' AM/AOS

Bulb. gracillimum (Rolfe) Rolfe
Peninsular Thailand to SW Pacific
Graceful heads of 3-4" flowers with thread-like sepals. Semi-rambling but
rewarding. Some clones are yellowish and some are ruby-red. No odor.

Bulb. falcatum (Lindl.) Rchb.f.   West Tropical Africa to Uganda
var. falcatum   West Tropical Africa to Uganda
var. velutinum (Lindl.) J.J.Verm.   W. & WC. Tropical Africa
The clone shown at the top is *var. falcatum*. At the bottom is *B. falcatum*
(the green form). The *var. velutinum* is much redder and has more flowers
open at one time. Easy to grow and flower. Plants very rambling. No odor.

Bulb. vaginatum (Lindl.) Rchb.f.
Peninsular Thailand to West and Central Malaysia
Common and easy to grow and bloom.
Most heads of flowers look like the top clone and are less uniform
than the bottom clone. Similar to *B. medusae*, but smaller number
of flowers and shorter sepals. Mild odor.

©Lewis Ellsworth

Bulb. katherinae 'A-doribil' CHM/AOS

Bulb. reticulatum Bateman ex. Hook.f.
(B. katherinae A.D.Hawkes is considered a synonym by some)
Mulu Cliffs of Sarawak, Borneo
Limestone cliff substrate means plants grow in an environment of high ph.
I put oyster shell fragments in the sphagnum to achieve this and the plants
grow well and bloom, whereas they died before. No odor.

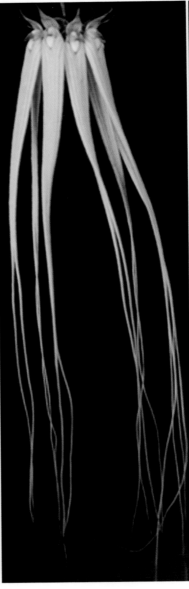

**'Yong's Burmese
Pink'**

©Jim Clarkson

'Yasnita'   'A-doribil Crown' FCC/AOS
Bulb. longissimum (Ridl.) J.J.Sm.
Burma to Thailand
Plant on the left is 23" long (58cm); center is 11" long (28cm).
Easy to grow and bloom. Flowers in the fall. Plants semi-rambling. Keep
flowers dry for longer life. Spikes pendant so hang plants up for better
presentation of blooms. Up to 4 spikes per bulb on robust plants. No odor.

Bulb. frostii Summerh.
Vietnam; clusters of 3cm flowers (up to 6, usually 2-4), olive-green bulbs with thick, shiny blue-green leaves. Bright light and lots of water during growing season, then a rest. Flowers in early summer in Florida. No odor.

©Donald Wilson

Bulb. guttulatum (Hook.f.) N.P.Balakr. 'D&B' AM/AOS
Himalaya to Vietnam
Umbels of up to 15 flowers on medium tall spikes. Flowers about 1 ½ cm with pretty spots and deep rose-red lip. Color pattern very dominant in breeding. Mild fragrance.

'A-doribil' AM/AOS

Bulb. bicolor Lindl.
Listed from SE China, but comes from Peninsular Thailand and Malaysia
Sub-umbels of up to 8 flowers with distinct in-rolled lateral sepals. Needs
a cooling and slight drying period in the winter to flower. Rambling (darn!).
Mild odor.
Top clone was used in the first hybrids, Stars And Stripes, Ed Gilliland,
Boon Bryson, Marv Ragan and A-doribil Candy.
Picture of the clone on the left above was sent to me for identification and I
don't know the owner. Would love to get a division for breeding.
Flower on the right above is the 'Kaylee Marie' AM/AOS clone.

©Lewis Ellsworth
'D&B 27' AM/AOS

©George Schudel
'D&B 27' CCM/AOS
Trias picta (C.S.P. Parish) C.S.P. Parish ex Hemsl.
Malaysia and Thailand
This plant has been put back into Bulbophyllums for registration purposes (sometimes) and is then called *Bulb. pictum*. Small blue-green leaved plants produce up to 8 flowers clustered at base of bulbs. Large flower segments have good potential in hybridizing. After seeing many specimens, I believe the top clone is a tetraploid.
Blooms in late winter after drying-out period. No odor.

Bulb. thiurum J.J.Verm. & P. O'Byrne   *Bulb. plumatum* Ames

These plants used to be thought of as color forms of the same species, but they are very different. Both come from Peninsular Malaysia, but the *plumatum* also comes from Sumatra and the Philippines. They flower throughout the year and produce flowers up to 10" (25cm) long. Small plants will flower with 4 bulbs. Close-ups in the center have had the dorsal sepals removed to show "fingers" on the petals, which are distinctive and occur in all the plants in the Rhytionanthes Section. No odor.

Bulb. ambrosia (Hance) Schltr.
Nepal to China
Small plant with olive bulbs and 3" (7cm) rectangular leaf. Penny-sized flowers are produced singly along the rhizome and have, (some say), a very pleasant fragrance. Easy to grow and flower.

Bulb. lasiochilum Par. & Rchb.f.   'D&B 31'
Myanmar (Burma) to Peninsular Malaysia
Large flower for small-sized plant. Lasts 3-5 weeks with no odor.

Sestochilus Section

©Ernest Walters

Bulb. lobbii Lindl. 'A-doribil Too' AM/AOS
India to the Philippines, Borneo and Indonesia
For culture, see Chapter 13. Mild odor some say is pleasant.

Bulb. lobbii 'Sorella'
This clone is from Palawan Island, Philippines
No odor.

Bulb. lobbii
This clone is from Malacca, Malaysia
From Andy Phillips. No odor.

©Ernest Walters

Bulb. lobbii 'Bronze Delight' AM/AOS
This clone is from Sumatra. No odor.

Bulb. smitinandii Seidenf. & Thorut
Indo-China
Wide-spaced bulbs with large, light green leaves. 3" (7.5cm) flowers have
distinctive pinching and stripes. Somewhat rare in culture, but very rewarding. Large bulbs and leaves. Rambling. Mild odor.

©Lewis Ellsworth

Bulb. sumatranum Garay, Hamer & Siegerist
'A-doribil' AM/AOS
Considered a synonym of *lobbii* by some. Flowers in many shades, blooms
throughout the year, has no odor and can be very floriferous.

'Raspberry'

'Goldie'

'Verry Berry'

'Louis Del Favero' on left
'Golden Galleon'   on right

'Lauris's Luck' HCC/AOS
Bulb. facetum Garay et al.
Philippines
Three clones shown here. Plants are semi-rambling. Grow in bright shade,
but they flower best in lower light. Wide segments and good form are
beneficial for breeding. Inflorescence is short, but crosses with plants in
Lepidorhiza Section are wonderful (see B. Tonya Jacobs). Mild odor.

©Yanyong Punpreuk

Bulb. dearei (Rchb.f.) Rchb.f.
Peninsular Malaysia, Borneo to Philippines
Very easy to grow and bloom. Swept back petals can be overcome in
hybrids. Distinctive lip identifies the species easily. Somewhat rambling,
the 3" (7cm) flowers have no odor.

Hyalosema Section

©Don Wilson

Bulb. burfordiense Garay et al.
Papua New Guinea
Awarded as *Bulb. grandiflorum* 'D&B 27'
This was separated from *grandiflorum* due to the hairs on the lip, which are lacking on *burfordiense*. Also, *grandiflorum*, as its name implies, is a very large flower. Culture and clonal differences can make the two overlap, so identification from that criterion is discouraged. It flowers along the rhizome throughout the year and can take fairly bright light, as the thick leaf suggests. No odor.

Bulb. burfordiense 'A Friend'   *Bulb. burfordiense* 'Irian Jaya 1st'
Plant on left belongs to a mysterious and shy bulbo grower in Memphis who wishes to remain anonymous. Flower is about 7" (18cm) long. Flower on right is about 6" (15cm) long.

Bulb. grandiflorum Blume
Malaysia to Solomon Islands
This, I believe, is the true grandiflorum, called *B. cominsii* by some.
No odor.

Bulb. fritillariiflorum J.J.Sm.
New Guinea
The name refers to the markings on the sepals. Medium sized flower produced sporadically through the year. Stiff, upright leaves tell you it likes
brighter light. Dorsal sepal covers stigmatic surface so it isn't affected by
rain during flowering. Pollinated by small flies or gnats (probably). No odor.

Bulb. arfakianum Kraenzl.
From the Arfak Mountains in West New Guinea. Plants and flowers are much smaller than either *B. burfordiense* or *B. grandiflorum*, as well as being shaped differently. Mild odor.

Bulb. fraudulentum Garay et al.
West New Guinea
3" flowers produced all through the year. Does NOT like to get water on buds or they rot. Set in shallow tray of water when in bud to allow flowers to become their best. Easy to grow and bloom. Mis-identified as *B. arfakianum* and *B. fritillariiflorum*. No odor.

Large plant in bud.
Getting the flowers wet at this time will cause them to drop.

Umbel types

Bulb. longiflorum Thouars
Tropical Africa through to Indonesia and Pacific
Most widespread of all the bulbophyllums. 1st species called a
Cirrhopetalum. Criteria were: hairs on dorsal sepal and petals,
lateral sepals rotated and OUTSIDE margins fused and FLAT.
Comes in a variety of colors with or without spots. No odor.

Bulb. elegans Gardner ex Thwaites
SW India and Sri Lanka
Rambling habit but worth it. Up to ten, medium-large (2-3"; 5-7cm)
flowers in umbels. This is the 'Krull-Smith' clone.
Distinctive "lure" on the dorsal sepal helps to attract the pollinators.
Blooms in the spring through summer. No odor.

Bulb. flabellum-veneris (J.Konig) Aver.
Indo-China to West and Central Malaysia and Philippines
This has been called *B. lepidum* for decades, but this is the true name.
Sometimes called *B. gamosepalum*, but sorting them all out will take more time. Plants incorrectly called B. Daisy Chain are also this species. Very easy to grow and bloom, producing up to 5 inflorescences per bulb on robust plants. Blooms throughout the warmer months of the year. If grown outside, often pollinated by fungus gnats. No odor.

Two other clones of the species.
Short-lived flowers but quick to repeat bloom.

Bulb. dolichoblepharon (Schltr.) J.J.Sm.
Philippines, Sulawesi to the Moluccan Islands
Up to 20 small flowers (1½", 3cm) on long wiry stems. Flowers early to late summer MANY times. Plants somewhat rambling. No odor.

Bulb. cumingii (Lindl.) Rchb.f.
Sabah, Borneo to the Philippines
Flowers of this clone, 'Tower Grove' CBR/AOS, from Marilyn LeDoux are 2" (5cm) and actually this hot-pink color. Plants are small and bloom throughout the summer into fall. Easy to grow and bloom. No odor.

160

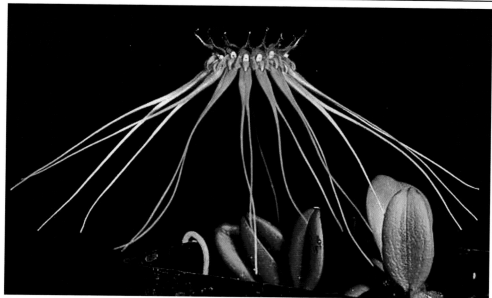

©Edwin S. Boyett

Bulb. tingabarinum Garay et. al. 'Rainbow' CBR/AOS
From Taiwan, SE China, Laos and Vietnam.
Considered a synonym of *B. pecten-veneris* (Gagnep.) Seidenf.. This clone belongs to Bob Fallon in Alabama. Either way, it is a super flower that blooms on small plants several times a year in the warmer months. No odor.

Bulb. loherianum (Kraenzl.) Ames 'A-doribil' CHM/AOS
Philippines
Small jellybean bulbs with a shiny stiff leaf produce up to 4 spikes per bulb with 20 flowers each throughout the summer into fall.
Flowers are 1" (2.5cm). No odor

©Jim Clarkson

Bulb. annandalei Ridl.
Peninsular Thailand to Peninsular Malaysia
Semi-rambling plants flower all summer and again in the winter when ro-
bust, producing up to 4 spikes per bulb. This clone received a First Class
Certificate from the AOS and is the parent of many new hybrids. Flowers
range from clear yellow to orange with red stripes. No odor.

Bulb. sanguineopunctatum Seidenf. & A.D. Kerr
Laos
This isn't a true umbel type, but I like it a lot. Up to 20, 3-to-4 inch long flow-
ers jammed into a cluster. Plants are semi-small and striped flowers come
in several shades of cream to dark pink with contrasting white fringe.
No odor.

Bulb. wendlandianum (Kraenzl.) J.J.Sm.
Indo-China (Burma, Thailand)
Distinctly different from *B. rothschildianum.* See Chapter 10. No odor.

AOS Award photo; no photographer listed

Bulb. rothschildianum (O'Brien) J.J.Sm.
Darjeeling (maybe) to Assam; see chapter 10
'Red Chimney' AM/AOS 81 points

Probably the most famous of all the Bulbophyllums, and one of the most spectacular. This is the 'Red Chimney' clone. It first received an Award of Merit of 81 points when exhibited in 1976 by Ronald Sellon of Oregon, then was elevated to a First Class Certificate of 91 points when exhibited in 1991 by Owen Neils of Michigan. It reached its apogee (highest point) when exhibited by Frank Smith of Krull-Smith Nursery and he was given a Certificate of Cultural Excellence of 97 points in 1997. Most plants available up to 2003 were divisions of this clone and perhaps 2 or 3 others. A population produced between this clone and the 'A-doribil' FCC/AOS clone has made seed-grown plants available to the public. The 4th generation is in the lab now (mid 2009). See Chapter 10. No odor.

AOS Award photo; no photographer listed
'Red Chimney' FCC/AOS 91 points

©Johanna Tjeenk Willink
'Red Chimney' CCE/AOS 97 points

**This clone came from Geoff Stocker
in Australia, and grew larger
as the plant grew bigger.**

©Donald Wilson

'A-doribil' FCC/AOS

'Kaylee Marie' HCC/AOS
F2 generation =('Red Chimney' X 'A-doribil')

165

'Frank's Favorite'
F3 generation from ('A-doribil' X F2)
F2 = 'Kaylee Marie' HCC/AOS =('Red Chimney' X 'A-doribil')

Mastigion Section*

©Yanyong Punpreuk

Bulb.
putidum
'Pumpkin City'

Bulb.
fascinator
'Garnet Beauty'

Bulb.
fascinator
'Krull's
Perfection'
FCC/AOS

Bulb.
fascinator
'Yong's
Semi Albina'

Interesting new blue-purple
color form found in the
Philippines. Very large flower
produced on small plants.
Photo by Jun Salvanera

*see Chapter 10

167

Lepidorhiza Section

Bulb. echinolabium J.J.Sm.
Sulawesi Island (formerly the Celebes)

The biggest and most important species in the section for breeding. Extremely large flowers (up to 20", 50cm long) are produced in succession for months and rebloom a few months later on robust plants. Name refers to the protrusions on the bizarre lip. A sweet and friendly butterfly came by to inspect the flower and was reduced to a shriveled hulk in seconds by the overpowering stench of rotted fish stuffed in a dead rat and left in the sun for a week. Can be bred out in a few generations.

Bulb. carunculatum Garay et al.
Philippines
For almost 50 years, everyone around the world had divisions of this one plant, 'Magnifico' AM/AOS. It was brought to Japan by an enthusiast and the origin was lost to memory. It would not produce seed so everyone had to wait until it grew up large enough to divide. In the early 1990s, it was rediscovered in the Philippines and now there are many different clones and plants are being produced in the lab from a variety of color forms. Name refers to the bumps on the lip. Flowers are 4-5" (10-12cm) tall. Mild odd odor.

©Ernest Walters
'A-doribil' AM/AOS

'Kaycee' HCC/AOS
plant from Mike Heinz

Bulb. sulawesii Garay et al.
Sulawesi Island
The photo isn't wrong, the flower is produced horizontally like this.
Distinctive hairs on the lip must help the pollinators which are probably
large bees. Flowers are from pale cream to this raspberry-red color
and up to 8" (20cm) long. Mild odor.

Bulb. basisetum J.J.Sm.
Philippines
Name refers to the bristles on the back of the lip. 3-4" (7-10cm) flowers are
produced on 5-8" (12-20cm) long horizontal inflorescences. No odor. Just
kidding, the rich, dark red flowers are, unfortunately, very stinky.

Bulb. cootesii M.A.Clem.
Philippines
Named after Jim Cootes from Australia.
3" (7cm) tall flowers come in clear yellow to orange with stripes and open at
the same time, unlike many of the others in this section. Mild odor.

Bulb. klabatense Schltr.
Sulawesi Island
Small flower (2", 5cm) but produced in succession for up to 9 months from
mid-winter to the fall. No odor.

***Bulb. paluense* Higgins**
From Sulawesi Island
Shiny 3-4" (7-10cm) flowers are produced for up to 6 months
from spring to the fall. Mild odor.

***Bulb. mearnsii* Ames 'A-doribil' AM/AOS**
Philippines
Very shiny 3 inch flowers in bronze and orange with
swept-back petals and spots.
Mild smell. Flowers from early spring through the summer.

Bulb. orthoglossum Kraenzl.
Philippines
Name refers to the red lip. Flowers up to 4" (10cm) tall produced for 2-4
months in the spring through the summer. No odor.

Bulb. levanae Ames
Philippines
3" (7cm) flowers are very stinky. Produced on lateral inflorescences for
about 6 weeks in the summer, where the heat helps to make the bad smell
more lingering. There is much confusion in this section, with mis-identifi-
cations and overlapping synonyms. At times, the plant on the left has been
called B. recurvilabre, the one on the right, B. trigonosepalum.

© Donald Wilson

Bulb. mandibulare **Rchb.f.**
Sabah, Borneo
This is the D&B' CHM/AOS clone. Flower form (closed) and presentation
(pendulous) kept it from being a good candidate for hybridizing, until the
potential of an open flower was considered. Fred Clarke convinced me to
attempt a few crosses to see if the problems could be overcome.
Segment width is very good, substance is heavy and color is deep
and rich. Not all clones are this closed. Plants are 2-3 years from
blooming (mid 2009), so we will see. Mild odor.

Bulb. papulosum **Garay**   **Philippines**
The last in this Section (for which I have photos), is alternately called this for
the bumps on the lip and lateral sepals, or *B. recurvilabre*, for the recurved
lip. I believe this is the correct name. Dr. Garay identified this and my plant
of *B. recurvilabre* as the same species, but they are very different in the
flower form, style of blooming and plant habit.

Macrobulbum Section

The species in this section all come from New Guinea. Four of them are quite large, two of which are gigantic, with leaves that can grow up to 6 feet (2 meters) long and bulbs that can get up to the size of large grapefruit.

©Greg Allikas

Bulb. orthosepalum **J.J.Verm. 'A-doribil' CHM/AOS**
East New Guinea
Name refers to the red sepals. Medium size and easy to flower
several times a year. 4" (10cm) flowers very stiff. Mild odor. A synonym is
B. hashimotoi. Bulbs the size of oranges and leaves to 3 feet long (1 meter).

Bulb. phalaenopsis **J.J.Sm.**
Throughout New Guinea
Most common and largest of the section. Yellow hairs on the flowers
identify the species and are probably an attractant for the flies that pollinate
them. Odor of rotting meat. This head of flowers was the size of a football.

Bulb. fletcherianum Rolfe
New Guinea
This is the accepted name of two species, one of which is named *B. spiesii*.
The original described plant of *B. fletcherianum* only had about 7 flowers, so
when Dr. Leslie Garay was shown a specimen that had dozens of flowers, he
felt it was a new species. There is not enough difference beside the flower
count to justify a new name, so, it stays. Foul odor.

© E. "Chaps" Chapman
My trophy wife, Dorie, with 150-pound plant

Bulb. macrobulbum J.J.Sm.
New Guinea
This is the best of the section. This clone, 'Magnifico' AM/AOS has received almost every award that can be given to a species. The plants are medium sized, flower several times a year, have only a mild odor and are very floriferous with wide open flowers. I am trying to obtain a different clone to make an outcross and grow a population of more plants, so if you have one, PLEASE CONTACT ME.

177

Bulb. agastor Garay, Hamer & Siegerist
East New Guinea
This one is small compared to the others. Leaves aren't much longer than 12" (30cm) and it blooms 2-3 times a year. This plant ('Magnifico' CBR/AOS) is in a 5" (12cm) pot. No odor.

There is one other in the Section, *Bulb. cruentum* Garay, et. al., the smallest of them all and one which I have been unable to grow for very long. All the plants I have received look burnt by the sun or fires and don't live long. Yanyong Punpreuk (Yong) in Thailand seems to be able to grow them long enough to flower, as well as a shy and mysterious grower from Memphis, Tennessee.

178

Chapter 14
The Hybrids

In orchids, primary crosses (a cross between two species) produce blooms among the seedlings which are very similar. This is somewhat contrary to the conventional wisdom about Mendelian Inheritance, which was suggested by Gregor Mendel in 1864 and 1865. Most think the offspring of a cross would be segregated into: 25% like one parent, 25% like the other parent and 50% hybrid between the two. After doing extensive work with pea plants and with plants having white and purple flowers, he came up with the understanding of dominant and recessive traits.

What actually happens is much different, and completely unknown ahead of time since there are many genes, they work individually and in groups and what is dominant or recessive isn't known until many pairings with different parents. Also, a white flower might be a true albino (which is recessive), or it might be a hybrid of both dominant and recessive genes and be masking the colored parent. And this example is just for color. There are many other traits and what is dominant and recessive changes from plant to plant.

Consequently, many of the first bulbo hybrids had very little variation in the flowers among the progeny (seedlings). The dominant characteristics show up in a 3:1 ratio in the f2 generation (second filial) and we are growing only a small percentage of the seeds (usually). Add to this the fact that we are using plants that have been crossed and recrossed for hundreds of years (in the wild) before we use them as a parent and you can see why it is impossible to predict what will appear before the cross is made the first time. After several populations are made, it is possible to state fairly certainly that, for instance, using *Broughtonia sanguinea* (Sw.) R.Br. as a parent will result in a hybrid with roundish flowers clustered at the end of the stem, or using *Brassavola nodosa* (L.) Lindl., will result in flowers that have thin, pointed segments.

In the subsequent generations bloomed so far, there is a greater variation among the seedlings (mostly in color) and there will undoubtedly be even more in the future as crosses build up a more diversified gene pool.

Since there are only a little over 200 hybrids registered in Bulbophyllums so far, there are plenty of opportunities for new and exciting things. Don't be afraid to try your hand at it yourself.

A wonderful guy in Houston, Texas, Jay Balchan, crossed two flowers that were open in his greenhouse and made one of the best crosses to date, named after his wife, Tonya Jacobs (*facetum* X *echinolabium*).

Bulb. facetum   **Bulb. echinolabium**

© Brian Kelly

**Bulb. Tonya Jacobs
'A-doribil' HCC/AOS**

© Brian Kelly

**Bulb. Tonya Jacobs
'Dorie's Delight' AM/AOS**

You don't have to dig too deeply to mine gold in this genus.

Here are some of the early crosses:
Sanders Orchids registered the first hybrid,
B. Louis Sander (*longissimum X ornatissimum*), in 1936
along with B. Fascination (*longissimum X fascinator*).

©Brian Kelly

**Bulb. Louis Sander
'A-doribil 59'**

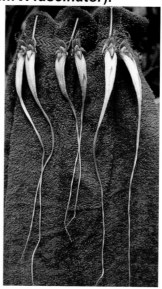

**Three different clones
of the real Louis Sander
showing 2 flowers each**

He then registered Bulb. David Sander (*lobbii X virescens*) in 1937 and those
were the only crosses until 1969, when Stuart Low Company registered
Bulb. Elizabeth Ann (*longissimum X rothschildianum*).

**Bulb. Elizabeth Ann
'Buckleberry'
FCC/AOS**

Eric Young Orchid Foundation on the Isle of Jersey, England really got everyone excited with a cross they registered in 1996 that was made by Michael Tibbs called Bulb. Jersey (*lobbii X echinolabium*).

Bulb. lobbii

Bulb. echinolabium

**Bulb. Jersey
'A-doribil'
AM/AOS**

©Allen Black

Bulb. Jersey 'Black's Red Star'

Starting in the mid 1990s, Suphachadiwong Orchids in Thailand registered many new hybrids using a variety of different species. Since then, a number of hybridizers have entered the field, among them are: Meen Orchids (Phongsawat Phinhiran, known as Oat) and Yanyong Punpreuk (Yong), in Thailand, Bill Williams in Australia and your humble scribbler in the United States, who has added quite a few as well and is working on many more. Now that it is better known what is dominant, it is easier to avoid going down the wrong roads. Of course, there are many un-traveled roads appearing just past the fog.

Here are some of the newer crosses that have been made.

Bulb. carunculatum   Bulb. lobbii
'Magnifico'   'Kathy's Gold'
CBR-AM   AM/AOS

Bulb. Frank Smith

'Golden Star'   'Orange Delight'

183

Bulb. Elizabeth Ann
'Buckleberry'
FCC/AOS

Cirr. rothschildianum
'Red Chimney'
FCC/AOS

©Mark Alan Reinke

©Mark Alan Reinke

Bulb. Lovely Elizabeth 'Marble Branch' AM-CCM/AOS

Bulb.
annandalei
'A-doribil'
AM-FCC 82 pts

©Brian Kelly

Bulb.
rothschildianum
'A-doribil'
FCC 91 pts

©Don Wilson

©Ernest Walters

Bulb. A-doribil Anna Roth 'Candy Stripe' AM/AOS

Bulb. A-doribil Anna Roth 'Cherry' AM/AOS

Cirr. rothschildianum
'Red Chimney'
FCC/AOS

©Lewis Ellsworth

Bulb.
fascinator
'Hilltop'

Bulb. Doris Dukes
AQ/AOS
'Bill's Choice' AM/AOS

This is the first bulbo cross to receive an Award of Quality, given to the entire cross, named after my wife, Dorie. I hope to produce many more. There are several in the wings that are candidates.

Bulb. rothschildianum
'Red Chimney'

Bulb. putidum

©Lewis Ellsworth

Bulb. Cindy Dukes 'D&B' AM/AOS

©Thomas McGuigan

Bulb. Cindy Dukes 'D&B' CCM/AOS
(*rothschildianum X putidum*)

Bulb. Doris Dukes   Bulb. *longissimum*

Bulb. Melting Point 'A-doribil'

Bulb. Doris Dukes
'Bill's Best' AM/AOS

Bulb. echinolabium
'A-doribil' AM/AOS

Bulb. A-doribil Collin 'Sublime' HCC/AOS

Bulb. A-doribil Collin 'Peppermint' HCC/AOS

Bulb. lobbii
'Kathy's Gold'
AM/AOS

Bulb. bicolor 'A-doribil'
AM 83 pts

Bulb. Stars And Stripes 'A-doribil' HCC/AOS

'A-doribil Too' HCC/AOS

Bulb. lobbii
'Kathy's Gold' AM/AOS

Bulb. claptonense
'D&B' CHM/AOS

© Jim Clarkson

Bulb. Jim Clarkson
'USF Botanical Gardens' AM/AOS

'A-doribil 63' AM/AOS

©Jim Clarkson
'Bill Thoms' FCC/AOS

©Pete Thompson
'Jackson Likens' FCC/AOS

Bulb. Stars and Stripes
'A-doribil' AM 82 pts

Bulb. echinolabium
'A-doribil'
AM 82 pts

©Lewis Ellsworth

©Lewis Ellsworth

Bulb. A-doribil Super Star 'A-doribil' AM/AOS

Bulb. A-doribil Super Star 'A-doribil Too' HCC/AOS

Bulb. carunculatum 'Magnifico' CBR-AM 82 pts

Bulb. bicolor 'A-doribil' AM 83 pts

Bulb. Ed Gilliland 'A-doribil'

Bulb. Elizabeth Ann
'Buckleberry'
FCC/AOS

Bulb. bicolor 'A-doribil'
AM 83 pts

Bulb. A-doribil Candy 'Super'

'Frank's Favorite' AM - CCM/AOS

Bulb. Mary Alice Underwood

'A-doribil' AM/AOS   'Bronze Dragon'

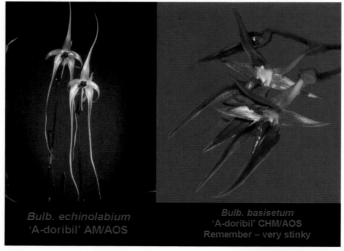

Bulb. echinolabium
'A-doribil' AM/AOS

Bulb. basisetum
'A-doribil' CHM/AOS
Remember – very stinky

Bulb. A-doribil Upwind
'Red Sunset' AM/AOS

'Red Bird'

Bulb. Jersey
'A-doribil' AM/AOS

Bulb. Vicky Leighty
'A-doribil' HCC/AOS

Bulb. orthoglossum

©Ernest Walters

Bulb. Elizabeth Ann

Bulb. lasiochilum 'D&B 31' CCM 90 points

**Bulb. Emly Siegerist
'A-doribil 52'**

A-doribil Too' HCC/AOS

Bulb. lobbii
'Kathy's Gold'
AM/AOS

Bulb. facetum

Bulb. Jan Ragan
'A-doribil' AM/AOS

Bulb. bicolor

Bulb. Louis Sander

Bulb. Marv Ragan

Bulb. lobbii 'Kathy's Gold' AM/AOS

Bulb. emiliorum 'Hilltop' CHM/AOS

©James Harris

Bulb. Madeline Nelson
'Gary Allen' HCC/AOS

This plant, grown by Madeline herself, has the wonderful clove smell from *B. emiliorum* and an exceptionally large flower as well!

Bulb. annandalei
'A-doribil' FCC

Bulb. Louis Sander
'Crownpoint' AM

Bulb. A-doribil Anna Lou

Bulb. Doris Dukes
'Bill's Best'

Bulb. bicolor 'A-doribil'

Bulb. Boon Bryson

Bulb. A-doribil Candy

©James Clarkson

Bulb. annandalei

Bulb. A-doribil Candy Ann

©Lewis Ellsworth

Bulb. sumatranum

Bulb. Star Of Sumatra

©Lewis Ellsworth

Bulb. echinolabium

**Originator; Dr. R. W. Quene, Registered by Jerry Fischer
This population made by me**

Bulb. echinolabium
'A-doribil' AM/AOS

Bulb. sulawesii
'Raspberry'

Bulb. JoAnne Hartzler

Bulb. Jersey
'A-doribil' AM/AOS

Bulb.
Valley Isle
Queen

©Lewis Ellsworth

Bulb. echinolabium

Bulb. sulawesii
'Raspberry'

Bulb. pictum
'D&B' AM/AOS
previously:
Trias picta

Bulb. A-doribil Sulapic

Bulb. lobbii
'Kathy's Gold'
AM/AOS

Bulb.
Ray Gabaldon

Bulb. burfordiense

Bulb. lasiochilum

Registered by
Neil Oyama

Bulb. Sheryl Kurizaki

Bulb. fascinator

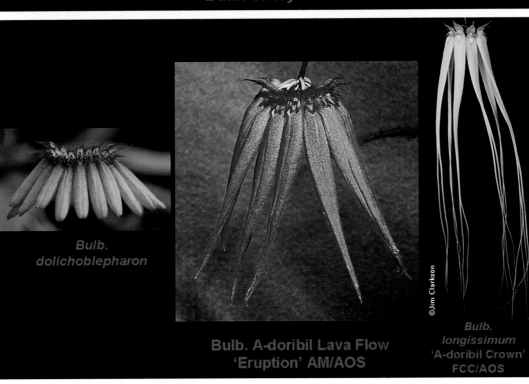

Bulb.
dolichoblepharon

©Jim Clarkson

Bulb. A-doribil Lava Flow
'Eruption' AM/AOS

Bulb.
longissimum
'A-doribil Crown'
FCC/AOS

©Charles Rowden

Bulb. frostii 'Yasnita'
HCC/AOS

Bulb. lepidum
(flabellum-veneris)

Bulb.
A-doribil Gem

©Charles Rowden

Bulb. frostii 'Yasnita'
HCC/AOS

Bulb. dentiferum

Bulb.
A-doribil
Ring

Bulb. frostii 'Yasnita'
HCC/AOS

Bulb. guttulatum
D&B' AM/AOS

Bulb.
Purple
Slippers

Bulb. rothschildianum

Bulb. frostii 'Yasnita'
HCC/AOS

Bulb.
Crownpoint
'A-doribil'
HCC

Bulb. Crownpoint was made by Marilyn LeDoux of Labadie, Missouri.
A wonderful hybridizer of many genera and a very classy lady. A
clone of this cross won the Best Bulbophyllum of the Year in 2008,
(the Bill Thoms Bulbophyllum Award given by the AOS).
This clone was a Blue Ribbon Winner at the 19th WOC in Miami.

Bulb. Elizabeth Ann
'Buckleberry' FCC/AOS

Bulb. Doris Dukes
'Bill's Best' AM/AOS

Bulb. Marilyn LeDoux

Bulb. sumatranum

Bulb. veitchianum

Bulb.
Jim McGoogan

Bulb. annandalei
'A-doribil' FCC/AOS

Bulb. claptonense
'D&B' CHM/AOS

©Jim Clarkson

©Lewis Ellsworth

Bulb.
Anna Clap

Bulb. gracillimum

Bulb. medusae

Bulb. Thai Spider

Bulb. falcatum 'Jade Green'

Bulb. purpureorhachis

Bulb. Sue Blackmore 'A-doribil'

Bulb. lobbii

Bulb. Nannu Nannu

Bulb. A-doribil LoNan

Cross made by Marilyn LeDoux

Bulb. Jiraporn Punpreuk
(*sanguineopunctatum X annandalei*)
Cross registered by Yanyong Punpreuk of Thailand
This population made by Jay Balchan of Houston, Texas

Hybrids from Bill Williams, Australia
All photos by Mr. Williams

Bulb. Wilmar Galaxy Star
(*dearei X lobbii*)

211

Bulb. Wilmar Candy Stripes
(*facetum* X Wilmar Galaxy Star)

#2

#3

Bulb. Wilmar Fantasy
(*basisetum* X Wilmar Galaxy Star)

#2

Bulb. Wilmar My Girl
(Wilmar Galaxy Star X *sulawesii*)

Bulb. Wilmar New Generation
(*graveolens* (F.M. Bailey) J.J.Sm. X *affine* Wall. Ex Lindl.)

Bulb. Wilmar Sheer Magic
(*digoelense* X Wilmar Galaxy Star)

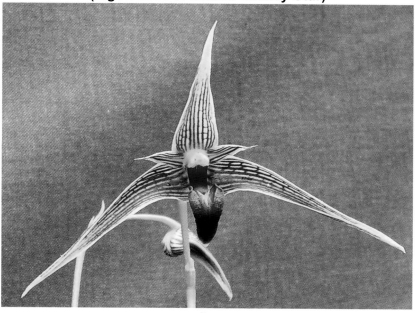

#2

Bulb. Wilmar Gee Whiz
(*dearei X affine*)

#2

Bulb. Wilmar Sunrise
(Fascination X *rothschildianum*)

Hybrids from Yanyong Punpreuk in Thailand
All photos by Mr. Punpreuk

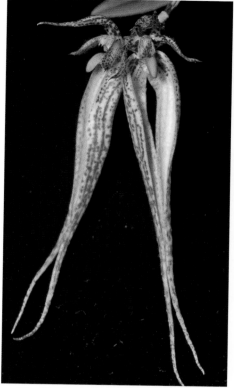

B. Eakachai Punpreuk
(*longissimum x lasiochilum*)

B. Tee Sprite Claw
(*putidum x annandalei*)

B. Jittraprun Piluek
(*sanguineopunctatum*
x disciflorum*)

*also called
Trias disciflora

217

B. Tee Siam Honey
(*annandalei x lobbii*)

B. Tee Honey Dew
(*annandalei x cupreum* Lindl.)

B. Tee Vincent Yap
(*annandalei x picturatum*)

B. Pranom Prutpongse   **#1**
(*sanguineopunctatum x bicolor*)

B. Tee Blush
(*tricorne* Seiden. & Smit.
x *longissimum*)

Hybrids from Phongsawat Phinhiran (Oat) in Thailand (Meen Nursery)
all photos by Oat (except Meen Mekong Lullaby)

B. Meen Bulbul
(lasiochilum x smitinandii)

B. Meen Garuda
(lasiochilum x echinolabium)

B. Meen Leopard Cubs
(lasiochilum x picturatum)

B. Meen Legend Jewel
(lasiochilum x bicolor)

B. Meen Indocine Boy
(*appendiculatum*
x coweniorum J.J.Verm. & P. O'Byrne)

B. Meen Mellow Moon
(*coweniorum x echinolabium*)

B. Meen Sri Nagara
(*fascinator x smitinandii*)

B. Meen Tarutao Pirate
(*appendiculatum x patens*)

B. Meen Endless Love
(*longissimum x bicolor*)

**B. Meen
Ocean Brocade**
(*longissimum x frostii*)

B. Meen Sassy Girl
(*flabellum-veneris
x vaginatum*)

B. Meen Cinnamon Witch
(*appendiculatum x bicolor*)

B. Meen Rainbow Rider
(*sanguineopunctatum x bicolor*)

©JoAnne Klein

B. Meen Mekong Lullaby
(*lepidum* x retusiusculum*)
*correctly: flabellum-veneris

B. Meen Treasure Sack
(*annandalei x disciflorum*)

Chapter 15
THE FUTURE

WHAT DOES THE FUTURE HOLD?

Well, at this point (2009), there are 212 hybrids made in the entire bulbo-phyllum genus. It is a group that is as large as the other two main BIGGIES in the orchid world, Dendrobiums (with over 7000 hybrids) and Pleurothallids (with over 2200 hybrids).

It's a gigantic field and the surface has just been scratched. There will, no doubt, wind up being a small number of plants that are the most influential and the most useful. These most surely will include *lobbii, facetum and sumatranum*; *echinolabium* and *carunculatum*; *rothschildianum, annandalei, longissimum* and *fascinator*, as well as others in the small umbel type such as *flabellum-veneris, cumingii* and *loherianum*. I haven't spent much time on *medusae, gracillimum* and flowers like those, but they are also important.

Plants in the Lepidorhiza Section mostly have large flowers, bloom for months (several days at a time), have close-growing plants and odd shaped flow-ers. The fact that they are pretty stinky will be overcome in future generations. Plants in the Sestochilus Section have fairly large flowers, good substance and bloom all along the rhizome sporadically throughout the year. There are roughly 15 species in each of these groups so there are potentially over 200 crosses in these sections alone.

The Cirrhopetalum Section (*lepidum* [correctly *flabellum-veneris*], *longi-florum, elegans*, etc.) flowers over, and over, and over, and over. Currently, they are primarily in the straw/peach/pink colors. If they could be turned into different colors using *B. dolichoblepharon* (for deep reds) or *B. cumingii* (for hot pinks) or *B. loherianum* (for bright yellows), that is sure to be an interesting avenue. These are easily grown and flower over a long period of time. They all grow under the same conditions and flower throughout the year.

Another avenue involves the *B. fascinator* and *B. longissimum* flowers. Trying to produce a plant that has growths that are closer together (because at times they can be quite rangy) would be beneficial. Andy Phillips of Andy's Or-chids in California has a clone of *longissimum*, 'Yasnita', which I flowered with sepals 23 inches (58cm) long! The inflorescences of *longissimum* are produced horizontally and are pendulous which can be a problem since they grow into the plant beside them unless they are hanging (which is how they grow in nature). A few new clones coming out of Indonesia have more upright spikes so perhaps this can be overcome.

The *B. fascinator* grows bulbs fairly close together although some clones can spread out. Frank Smith grew some select plants from a selfing I made of the 'Cathedral' clone and one received a First Class Certificate in the fall of 2007 ('Krull's Perfection') which was 10 inches long (25cm), that's almost twice as long as other clones. Selfings and outcrosses from these and others are coming out of the lab and should greatly improve the stock. Yanyong Punpreuk in Thailand has a couple of semi-albina clones which have great potential, and I came across a clone in the Philippines that has a flower almost blue in color. As always, remaking the early crosses with improved forms should do great things for the subsequent hybrids.

There are plants in the lab of a remake of B. Fascination (*longissimum X fascinator*) using two FCC clones (*longissimum* 'A-doribil Crown' and *fascinator* 'Krull's Perfection') that should produce some great plants. (At least until plants bloom, you can always expect to produce the next super Award of Quality hybrid!)

More of the *B. katherinae* (which is considered a synonym of *B. reticulatum* Bateman ex Hook.f.) simply for its beautiful leaves will always be worthwhile. The plants have an interesting flower but the leaves themselves are fabulous looking and growing up a population of them from seed would be helpful. That would be darn financial too because everyone loves them. They come from the limestone Mulu cliffs in Sarawak, Borneo and need to have oyster shells added to the mix so the ph stays high.

Using several of the Lepidorhiza species (*echinolabium, carunculatum, sulawesii*, etc.) onto various hybrids seem to be great avenue since it enlarges the flowers, gives more flowers over a longer time and keeps the plants from rambling.

Plants in the Section Careyana that have the flowers in elongated pinecones look like good candidates for interesting crosses having many flowers in interesting colors with a new flowering style (see B. Tee Blush).

So far, there has been little or no use of many species with interesting flowers such as *B. sigaldiae*, or *B. dayanum* with their hairy flowers, or *B. kermesinum*, *B. unitubum* and *B. antenniferum* (Lindl.) Rchb.f., with the strange knobs on their petals.

Bulb. kermesinum

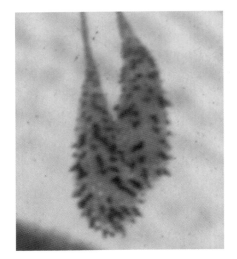

Bulb. unitubum

Bulb. antenniferum

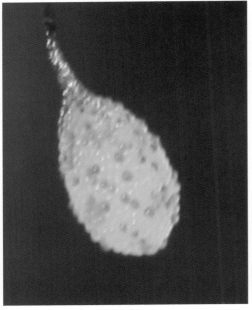

petal knob

Bulb. biflorum   Bulb. elassoglossum   Bulb. pardalotum

B. biflorum has double flowers and knobs on the lateral sepals, and *B. pardalotum* and *B. elassoglossum* Siegerist, with their large flowers for the size of the plants are good candidates. The interesting qualities may or may not be carried to the progeny, but only by growing a population of each will we find out. There are also the fuzzy and almost blue colors in *B. lindleyanum* Griff., as well as the blue-purple form of *B. fascinator* from the Philippines.

©Jun Salvanera
Bulb. fascinator
'A-doribil Blue'

Bulb. lindleyanum

Bulb. comosum
Collett & Hemsl.

close-up of flowers

Here is an interesting plant from Myanmar to Vietnam that goes dormant in the winter. While dormant, it produces 4 to 10 inch long racemes of white bristly flowers that last for many weeks. It might be an interesting parent, only experimentation will tell.

There are many fine species that haven't even been discovered, let alone used in breeding, so there are still lots of roads to explore. Don't be shy about trying your own ideas and go forth and multiply!!

This journey is still...

INCOMPLETE!!

On another note, I am working on a different book. During the months of December, 2008 and January, 2009, I had planned on going to the islands of Sulawesi and western New Guinea (Irian Jaya). My desire was to see bulbos in the wild and observe their growing conditions firsthand.

Dorie suggested I keep a journal, take lots of pictures and write a book about my travels when I returned which I thought was a good idea.

After speaking with several people about whom might be the person to help with the logistics of this, I was sent to Hans Herman in Bangkok, Thailand, and plans were made to send me to many of the places I wished to go, along with a guide/interpreter, collector, vehicle and accommodations.

I had to wire money ahead of time to cover extensive air flights for us all as well as daily money for the crew.

I was cheated out of the money by Hans who used the money for his own purposes and I was unable to go to these islands.

I was put in touch with the Salvanera family in the Philippines, (Rey, the father, Aida, the mother and Jun, the son who was my helper, interpreter and became my good friend). I spent almost 2 months going all over the islands of the Philippines with Jun seeing bulbos in the wild (and it was wild).

We met many of the local chiefs of the tribes who all had their own stories of being cheated by Hans, who seems to have cheated just about everyone with whom he has dealt.

DO NOT HAVE ANY DEALINGS WITH THIS LOSER!!!

The Salvaneras couldn't have been nicer, more honest or more helpful. Without them, my trip would have been a disaster and I would have quickly come home with nothing. As it was, I had a super time and saw many things which I will chronicle in a forthcoming book. (Jun's email is: rlsalvaneraiii@yahoo.com).

Please heed my words and beware of Hans, who, at 600+ pounds, has nothing else to do but figure ways to part you from your money. He is very believable, but aren't all con men?

Index

F

Fer-de-lance
  see Bothrops atrox 16
FOGG IT® 39
Fusarium 36

G

Gardener's Chronicle 93, 94, 96, 101
grex 9

H

HYDROGEN PEROXIDE 3% 73

I

International Orchid Registrar 10

K

Kew Bulletin 114
Klett, Kathy 9

L

LIQUID SEVIN 74

M

Madagascar 15
Mastigion 9
Megaclinium 9, 15

N

NEEM OIL 72

O

Orchid Genera in Thailand V111 109
Orchid Review 104
Orchids Australia 126
Orchids of Sikkim and N. E. Himalaya 116
Orchids of Sikkim and North East Himalaya 102
Oreos 41
outcross 78

P

pedicel 16
People